279

Books

HUGH TROWELL

The Unfinished Debate
on Euthanasia

SCM PRESS LTD

334 01726 2

First published 1973
by SCM Press Ltd
56 Bloomsbury Street London

© SCM Press Ltd 1973

Printed in Great Britain by
W & J Mackay Ltd, Chatham

CONTENTS

PREFACE

In 1970 I accepted the invitation of Professor Sir Ronald Tunbridge, Chairman of the British Medical Association Board of Science and Education, to chair a special panel to study euthanasia. Our panel was composed of some ten members, all of whom had special experience in this field, and we held numerous meetings throughout the year. There were those who cared for patients in the teaching hospitals or in general practice; some had specialized experience in geriatric wards or in institutions that cater for those suffering from severe incurable disease, while others had the care of sick children in paediatric wards. Our deliberations were helped by members of the administrative staff of the British Medical Association.

Right from the very beginning I insisted that we must study the case that had been made for the legalization of voluntary euthanasia, including all the relevant literature. At an early stage we invited the officers of the Voluntary Euthanasia Society to state their case, and on a subsequent occasion we received a small medical delegation of some doctors who supported the view held by that Society, namely that the law should permit voluntary euthanasia in certain circumstances.

All the members of the special panel were able to agree to the short report which was duly signed, presented to and adopted by the Council of the British Medical Association in January 1971, and published as a small brochure entitled *The Problem of Euthanasia*. As such it stands at the end of this book (Appendix A).

After the report had appeared, I felt it would be a pity if the large amount of material gathered were not recorded in some way or other. Acting therefore in a purely personal capacity and without reference to my colleagues on the special panel, and not in any way speaking for the British Medical Association, I thought it would be of value to write this individual expression of my views. This seemed desirable if only by reason of the fact that few other doctors have in recent years attempted to do this. When my own book had been finished I was glad to receive the book prepared as a joint venture by the Catholic Union and the Guild of Catholic Doctors in Great Britain, entitled *Your Death Warrant?*, ed. Jonathan Gould and Lord Craigmyle (Geoffrey Chapman 1971). Their approach is different from mine, for rightly or wrongly I decided from the very beginning to address myself to the ordinary Englishman, one who bears no allegiance to any particular religious point of view. He is at least entitled to the facts of the situation, distressing as these may appear to be. I have therefore excluded from the body of my book any arguments based on religious considerations. This however leaves the fundamental question – to be or not to be – unanswered, and so I have on the very last page put forth, somewhat tentatively, my own point of view, my outlook on life and my hope in death.

I hesitate to name the many persons who have helped my enquiries, or read portions of my manuscript, lest it should be considered that they agree with me, but I must thank Dr Cicely Saunders of St Christopher's Hospice and Dr Richard Lamerton of St Joseph's Hospice, who read some chapters and made most helpful criticisms out of their experience. Thanks are due to the Institute of Religion and Medicine, whose Study Secretary I was, for defraying the cost of this enquiry, and also to Dr Derek Stevenson, Secretary of the British Medical Association, for permission to print *The Problem of Euthanasia* as Appendix A, and to the Rev. A. B. Downing, Chairman of the Voluntary Euthanasia Society, for allowing me to print *Doctors and Euthanasia* as Appendix B. But finally the book remains in every sense of the word a personal expression of my own views concerning the unfinished debate.

I

History of Suicide and Euthanasia

Suicide

It is impossible to consider the history of euthanasia without that of suicide. From time immemorial one of the reasons for suicide has been incurable painful disease. More recently an investigation into the causes of suicide in London considered that the principal factor was physical illness in 18 %, mental disorder in 37 % and social factors in 35 %.[1]

Recent studies by numerous anthropologists in different parts of the world have testified to the fact that suicide has been regarded with dread and horror in almost all tribes.[2] The degree of disapproval has however varied considerably. Statements have even been made that some people, such as certain ancient tribes in Germany, accepted it calmly,[3] but it is difficult to check the validity of these reports.

Among underdeveloped peoples physical illness was at one time a cause of suicide and something akin to euthanasia was practised. Anthropologists state that this may even have been encouraged. At first those who were physically sick were helped by their relatives; later if the illness appeared to be incurable the sufferer became isolated.[4] Sometimes euthanasia may have been practised with the patient's consent, but at other times he may have been dragged unwillingly out of the hut and left to be eaten by wild animals.[5]

It is proposed in what follows to study the development of thought concerning suicide and euthanasia in the Western world. Reference will therefore be made mainly to Judaeo-Christian ideas, those of Greece and Rome and finally those of modern times. The teaching of the Eastern religions on these matters is considered very briefly, not because it is unimportant, having regard to the large number of persons involved, but because their attitudes have been summarized elsewhere.[6] The highest principles of Buddhism forbid suicide, for it violates the first of the five commandments, 'Kill not any living thing.' It is still permissible to offer one's life as a sacrifice by way of protest: this occurred when one Buddhist monk after another set fire to himself in South Vietnam in 1963.[7] Hinduism believes in reincarnation and has an ambivalent attitude towards suicide. Many Indians would condemn the practice, but the act of a holy man who fasts until death is admired. The whole continent of India felt the impact, as did the British government, whenever Gandhi fasted for political purposes. In Japan at one time *hara-kiri* was commended as a social custom for any disgraced nobleman or defeated general. This practice was made illegal in 1868. It is questionable whether these attitudes prevalent in the Far East reflect permissive religious teaching or merely social custom. Nothing is known of the attitude to the question of euthanasia.

When we turn to the forces that have moulded thought in the Western world, the first to be considered must be Judaism, as seen in the Old Testament, the Apocrypha and the Talmud. The suicides mentioned in the earlier books of the Old Testament were recorded with no open note of condemnation, though with tragic overtones. The tale was told of Samson, who had compromised himself by liaisons with foreign women so that his strength had gone. Fallen from power as the warlike leader of Israel and captured by the Philistines, he destroyed himself along with many of his enemies by pulling down the pillars of the building that held them all.[8]

The tragic story of King Saul, the first king of Israel, was punctuated by periods of depression. It ended in battle, when, mortally wounded, he asked his armour-bearer to despatch him, for he feared capture by the Philistines. When the man refused, some said that he fell on his sword,[9] though according to another version he was despatched by a foreigner, an Amalekite.[10] (Three other suicides by less heroic figures were the result of unsuccessful rebellion or even of wounded pride.[11]) These early books reflect the attitude in ancient Israel from, say, 1100 to 600 BC.

At some time after the exile in Babylon a subtle change occurred in the Jewish attitude to suicide, which might now be thought noble in those who died for the faith, though tragic in other circumstances. Possibly this change took place when the little state of Judah was incorporated into the Graeco-Roman world in the fourth century BC. An example of the new attitude was the self-immolation of Razis, who chose to commit suicide rather than surrender to foreign soldiers who were destroying the Jewish faith.[12] There were many martyrs in the second century BC, during the wars of the Maccabees.[13]

But the too ready acceptance of suicide in the Graeco-Roman world (discussed more fully below) probably stimulated a Jewish reaction against it, as against other Gentile attitudes. We meet an example of this in the Apocrypha, in the book of Tobit, an edifying fictional story written probably about 200 BC, where one of the characters, a girl afflicted by a demon, contemplates suicide; however, she puts the thought from her and instead prays for either death or deliverance, whereupon the archangel Raphael is sent to deliver her by magical means.[14]

Jewish repugnance to suicide had probably increased for some time before Josephus condemned it so trenchantly in the first century AD. He was not a religious leader but a historian, and his views reflected the current beliefs of pious Jews. The rabbis had searched the law of Moses in the Pentateuch and interpreted both the sixth commandment and other passages as condemning suicide.[15] These texts were further supported by sentiments expressed in some of the later writings of the Old Testament.[16] While none of these texts, at least to modern critics of the scriptures, appear explicitly to forbid suicide, they evidently carried considerable weight in the rabbinical exegesis of the first century AD. Josephus (AD 37–100), a Pharisee and the son of a priest, was the Jewish historian of the wars that culminated in the total destruction of Jerusalem by the Roman army in AD 70. He categorically condemned suicide in all circumstances, even in time of war. He spoke from personal experience, for he records an incident in which he and some other Jewish soldiers had been surrounded by the Roman legions. His companions had contemplated suicide, but this had been denounced by Josephus as a sin against nature and against God, who had entrusted life to man as a 'deposit'. Man should not lightly discard or do away with this 'deposit' from his Maker.[17] This view did not always prevail, however; Josephus also records, in the last desperate stages of the war, the mass suicide of the doomed Zealot garrison besieged in the fortress of Masada.[18]

The growth of the Christian teaching on suicide is more difficult to trace. Christianity arose within Judaism, and its attitude during the first century would be that of the Jewish apostles and converts. If

Josephus is any guide, then by that time an abhorrence of suicide was already prevalent among pious Jews. There are no words of Jesus or anywhere in the New Testament which condemn suicide or voluntary euthanasia, the hastening of death by active measures. (Those who in modern times have advocated voluntary euthanasia emphasize the point that the Bible, apart from the Apocrypha, adopts a non-committal attitude.) But Christians, searching the New Testament for texts bearing on suicide, have of course noted that Judas Iscariot hanged himself, and have deemed it an appropriate end, even if it was a sign of his remorse.[19] (The threatened suicide of the Roman jailer who thought that Paul had escaped from prison during an earthquake at Philippi[20] merely represents the normal Graeco-Roman attitude.) Even if the Bible does not explicitly condemn suicide, it usually places it in a most unfavourable setting.

Even before the fall of Jerusalem in AD 70 the Jews had been emigrating to many other countries, including all those that bordered upon the eastern Mediterranean. Faced with the rise of Christianity and conscious of the destruction of their own national life, the Jews held the more tenaciously to their ancient religion to preserve their identity. Their sacred books assumed an even greater importance: the law of Moses with the other books of the Hebrew Canon and their interpretation in the Talmud provided a stable foundation for their religion, morality and customs. To this day they remain the basis of any discussion of Jewish medical ethics, which has condemned euthanasia as 'plain murder'.[21] Their experiences of genocide under the Third Reich have made the term euthanasia stink in their nostrils. In time, however, the more secularly minded Jews may come to reconsider their attitude towards the termination of life in patients suffering from severe incurable disease.

But meanwhile among the Jews the influence of their sacred books tends to preserve a static attitude of rejection towards the question of euthanasia. Mohammedans too have their sacred book, the Koran, which expressly forbids the taking of human life in general terms. Numerous passages are sufficiently clear to forbid any deliberate killing of patients. Mohammedanism continues to regard suicide as a disgrace and euthanasia as abhorrent.[22]

All of this has a profound bearing on some of the problems which might arise if legislation on voluntary euthanasia were enacted for countries such as Britain and the United States, in fact most countries which contain a variety of religious groups. The attitudes of patients and relatives who ask for voluntary euthanasia and the decisions of doctors who might, if it were legalized, administer it, would be influenced to a considerable extent by conscience. However vague the concept of conscience may be, it has been found necessary to insert this word and idea into all Parliamentary bills that have proposed to legalize euthanasia in Britain. Conscience is much influenced by customary morality and by religion. It is therefore important to know the teaching of various religious groups on the question of suicide and voluntary euthanasia and to assess if possible the reactions of more modern groups, such as those who have diluted traditional religious attitudes with modern secularism. Religious views still carry weight. Thus a doctor who believed firmly in reincarnation might view euthanasia differently from an agnostic doctor who was equally convinced about personal extinction; both would differ from the Catholic doctor who regarded the final hours of a conscious dying person as influencing eternity.

The attitude of the Graeco-Roman world towards suicide and euthanasia was in many respects completely different from the developing Judaeo-Christian tradition. There had been many schools of thought in ancient Greece, and it is not possible to do justice to them here. Excellent reviews have been written, especially by those who support a tolerant attitude towards suicide and euthanasia.[23] Briefly speaking, a crude generalization would be that early Greek philosophers who held an exalted view of the Absolute opposed suicide; later philosophers who attached greater value to all that was human approved suicide, even commended it under certain circumstances. Amongst the former, Pythagoras in the fifth century BC had a profound reverence for life: man belonged to God. Socrates and his disciple Plato (427–347 BC) had a profound sense of the reality of the unseen world of ideas and 'forms'; suicide was therefore opposed, for man should stay at his post until the gods called. Suicide was however tolerated for extreme ill-fortune or distress. Aristotle (384–322 BC) a physician as well as a philosopher, considered suicide was unethical; he was to have a profound influence among scientists and doctors throughout the Middle Ages and until the Renaissance.

The Stoics, who came about a century after Aristotle, were of a different mettle. Then the flowering of Greek philosophy and science was on the wane and the city-states had degenerated into a broader internationalism that followed on the conquest of the Middle East by

Alexander the Great. Traditional Greek religion was declining, the gods no longer commanded respect, and the Stoics were to teach that man must look upon himself as rooted in the natural world; his duty was to follow nature. When man tired of life, he was free to take his departure: suicide could be a noble thing. Zeno, one of the founders of Stoicism, was said to have committed suicide because of a broken finger. The calm spirit of Stoicism was to prove very congenial to the martial but materialistic outlook of the Roman empire: it became its most popular religion for a period of five hundred years. In the first century AD Seneca, tutor to the young Nero, expressed a noble calmness when he said 'As I choose the ship in which I sail . . . so I will choose the death by which I leave life.'[24] He thought he could choose the ship of his departure, but he could not predict the storms on the ocean. Eventually he fell from favour and was dismissed by the Emperor with the result that he committed suicide (AD 65). A more lovable man, Epictetus, who lived his life in great simplicity in a small hut containing only a rush mat and an earthenware lamp, wrote: 'If the room is smoky, but only moderately, I will stay; if there is too much smoke, I will go.'[25] But the trouble he took, at the very end of his life, to rescue and provide for an infant exposed for death speaks louder than his words.

The Epicureans were a later and smaller group in the Graeco-Roman world. They made the pursuit of happiness their main aim and accepted suicide under adverse circumstances or for incurable disease. The Roman empire about the time of Christ represented a medley of beliefs that attempted to fill the void created by the death of the ancient gods and the decay of the pristine philosophies. Men craved for salvation, and exotic mystery religions such as that of Mithras, the cult of the slaughtered bull, crept in from the East, to fill the void. At that time it was recorded of the great Caesar Augustus that whenever he 'heard that someone had died quickly and without suffering he prayed for "euthanasia" for himself and his family'.[26] The word signified a quiet natural death; it was a prayer to the gods, not the physicians.

It is difficult to determine the degree of involvement of physicians in the Roman empire in assisting suicide for those sick in mind but not in body or in administering the lethal drug in voluntary euthanasia for those who had incurable disease. There are numerous examples of a doctor advising concerning the incurability of a complaint[27] and even supplying the poison,[28] but no passage has been traced in which physicians themselves administered the lethal draught, that is, voluntary euthanasia.[29] There were obvious reasons to counsel caution, especially in an age when justice was not above suspicion and political enemies were liquidated. A charge of murder could not be brought against a doctor unless he had administered the poison, so it was advisable for him to be absent from any scene of suicide. Even the issue of a lethal drug, perhaps at the request of a dying patient, could lead to slanderous accusations. Again it is difficult for people nowadays to realize that physicians in ancient Rome were often held in contempt, they engaged in menial dirty work, they were usually foreigners, often slaves; they would have to be very circumspect in giving poison to any Roman aristocrat. In severe incurable disease fasting unto death was a very popular form of euthanasia and it freed the family and physician from any charge of complicity.

Undoubtedly physicians in ancient Rome were involved in assisting suicide, even murder, by the issue of lethal drugs. It was probably against this practice that the Hippocratic oath for physicians was framed as a protest. 'I will neither give a deadly drug to anybody, if asked for it, nor will I make a suggestion to this effect. Similarly I will not give to a woman an abortive remedy.' Most have assumed that this oath reflected the ethical code of physicians not only of the Hippocratic school (fifth and fourth centuries BC) but throughout the Graeco-Roman world during the period of the Roman empire. The extensive researches of Edelstein have demonstrated convincingly that this oath never reflected the ethics of the Hippocratic school of physicians. Edelstein considered that the oath arose among the Pythagorean sect as a protest movement.[30] The ancient sect of the Pythagoreans had survived from the sixth century to the fourth century BC; it then died out almost completely, but revived in the first century AD. Its followers had a fanatical respect for all forms of life. As doctors they would not like to issue poison for suicide or murder, they would not like to be a party to an abortion, or even shed blood at an operation, all of which were forbidden in the Hippocratic oath.

The oldest known reference to the oath was in the first century AD;[31] it became popular in the medical schools of the Middle Ages since it was congenial to the Christian ethic on the sanctity of life. Up to the last century it was customary at many medical schools of Britain and the United States to ask students on qualifying to profess allegiance to the Hippocratic oath. The practice has died out but the influence exerted by this tradition is still strong.

A less well-known counterpart was the oath of Asaph; this was used among Jewish physicians in ancient times and stressed the same views on the sanctity of human life. Both oaths forbad physicians to assist murder and suicide. The oath of Asaph probably originated in the medical school of Syria between the third and sixth centuries AD. It contained these words 'Take heed not to kill any man with a root decoction,' and again, 'Do not mix a poison for any man or woman to kill his fellow man.'[32]

One can only conclude that both of these oaths and others recorded by medical historians[33] indicate that certain physicians in the Roman empire, many of whom were ignorant untrained practitioners,[34] did assist suicide, and even murder, by the issue of lethal drugs. It is probable that they would assist a person to commit suicide for incurable disease. Both the Hippocratic oath and the oath of Asaph arose as protests against this practice and were adopted in medical schools that found them congenial to their outlook.

There followed the centuries in which the Roman empire was decaying, coarseness and cruelty were common and gladiators fought to death in the arena. Infants were exposed to death and all Rome rejoiced when it heard of a massacre in some remote part of the Empire. The Graeco-Roman converts to Christianity also committed suicide all too easily and often for morbid reasons. Some were martyrs for the faith and were admired, others coveted martyrdom and provoked their heathen neighbours to murder them. Christian virgins committed suicide to escape rape. As the number of Christian martyrs rose so it became necessary to prevent any morbid sacrifice of life.

In North Africa life became very unsettled at the time of the break-up of the Roman empire. Members of the schismatic Donatist church allied themselves with marauding fanatic bands of peasants called Circumcelliones. These may be compared to the dervishes of modern times; they roved round the countryside in an aimless pilgrimage, singing and chanting in ecstasy. Possibly Augustine (AD 354–430) was basing himself only on exaggerated rumours,[35] but he wrote that some of these Christian 'hippies' cast themselves over cliffs to commit suicide.

It was against these wild excesses that Augustine as bishop of Hippo in North Africa set his face. He utterly condemned suicide, blaming the Stoics who condoned it.[36] Calling suicide under any circumstances 'a detestable and damnable wickedness' he interpreted the sixth commandment which forbad killing to include self-killing (*felo de se*). He also argued that suicide deprived a man of any possibility of penitence, meaning penitence for the suicide before he died. Life was a gift from God, in suicide a man rejected his Creator's gift. Finally Augustine said that suicide was often an act of cowardice, a way of retreat; he admitted however that it might sometimes be an act of bravery such as occurred among martyrs for the faith.

Augustine lived to see much of the Roman empire lapse into barbarism, the beginning of the Dark Ages. Most of the medical schools of the ancient world collapsed and the formal training of doctors ceased. The church survived and throughout these troubled times her attitude to suicide hardened, and the corpse of a suicide began to be dishonoured. During the next five centuries a succession of ecclesiastical decisions forbad the reception of oblations at the funeral mass of a suicide, then the singing of psalms, then any service and finally even the use of hallowed ground for burial. All this represented not only the teaching of Augustine but also an irruption of pagan beliefs expressing horror of suicide and fears of the corpse.[37] The burial of the corpse at the cross-roads with a stake through the heart and a stone on the head symbolized fears of the troubled lurking ghost. Suicide was a felony and all property became forfeit to the Crown. There were now vested interests, not all by any means ecclesiastical, which were desirous of retaining the penalization of suicide.[38]

During the Middle Ages the teaching of the Catholic Church was influenced by outstanding authorities like Augustine and to these were added eventually the great weight of Thomas Aquinas (1225-74). He maintained that suicide was contrary to nature because man desired to live. Man too had a debt to society and should not cancel his debt by suicide. Life too was given to man by God; it did not belong to man and was not his property; it was for God to determine when life should end.[39] The Catholic Church up to the present day has been consistent in its disapproval of suicide, although it has recognized in recent years that this may arise less culpably as a manifestation of mental disease. Its teaching stems from a steady and consistent weight of opinion and its belief that the Catholic Church is guided in these decisions. Voluntary euthanasia too has been categorically condemned in recent years. It is difficult to envisage any change in the Catholic teaching concerning voluntary euthanasia.

The Protestant tradition diverged somewhat from that of the

Catholic Church from the time of the Reformation. The condemnation of suicide remained unaltered, but when asked for their authority, Protestants laid less emphasis on the views of Augustine and Aquinas and more on an interpretation of the sixth commandment which forbad killing. On the whole they accepted uncritically the traditional abhorrence of suicide, but the Renaissance awakened an admiration for Greek and Roman ways of life and the ancient toleration of suicide provoked fresh thought. The poet Donne (1573–1631), later in life Dean of St Paul's, had written early in life a work which was published posthumously in which he had suggested that suicide might be justified under certain circumstances. The thin edge of the wedge was driven in.

The eighteenth century and the Age of Reason saw some of the rationalists questioning the religious assumptions on which the condemnation of suicide rested. David Hume (1711–76) dismissed the idea of an immortal soul and considered that a man might quite rationally commit suicide under certain conditions; this was not merely permissible; it might even be laudable. When the philosophy of the Enlightenment came to power in the French Revolution it repealed all sanctions of the state against the body and property of the suicide, measures followed slowly in other continental countries.

Traditional views which regarded suicide as sinful remained strong in Britain and North America until the present century. An increased study of suicide by psychiatrists and sociologists helped all sections of the community to see in suicide not so much a crime as a cry of distress or even the symptom of a psychiatric disorder. In England detailed studies in recent decades[40] and excellent reviews[41] have sown these ideas among a wider public. The inconsistencies of the law of the land and its harsh judgments were exposed by trenchant criticism.[42] An Anglican committee reported in 1959 and recommended that suicide and attempted suicide should cease to be a crime, but that a new law should in England make it a legal offence to aid, abet or counsel suicide. This was enacted in the Suicide Act (1961); suicide ceased to be a crime; those who aided suicide could be penalized and receive up to fourteen years imprisonment. Those who attempted to commit suicide ceased to be branded as felons; and no criminal proceedings were undertaken against them. Instead of this, doctors who had resuscitated anyone who had attempted to commit suicide referred the patients to a psychiatrist, a procedure rendered more easy since the passage of the Mental Health Act in 1959. A tolerant attitude towards suicide, often undertaken because of incurable disease, naturally led to a reassessment of the question of voluntary euthanasia, which is technically speaking an assisted suicide, under certain specified conditions.

Euthanasia

In recent centuries

Having considered the attitude of Western society to suicide from ancient times up to the present century, we now turn to review the growth of the modern movement to legalize voluntary euthanasia. The tolerant attitude towards suicide which characterized the Graeco-Roman world has already been mentioned.[43] The view has been expressed that some doctors in the ancient Roman empire may have issued lethal drugs to persons asking to commit suicide because they were distressed mentally or because they had incurable disease, but that the doctors probably seldom administered it themselves, thereby avoiding any charge of murder. Apart from this doctors in the ancient Graeco-Roman world were seldom, if ever, involved in the care of the dying. In fact they were advised not to touch them; they could not assuage pain or prolong life, death would only bring discredit upon the physician.[44]

Even in the Middle Ages physicians were seldom asked to visit the sick or the elderly in the various hospitals which had been founded by the church. Doctors were seldom appointed as wardens at any of these infirmaries. Dying and death were the concern of the priest, not that of the physician; the ability of the latter to help was negligible.[45]

After the Renaissance the status of physicians increased and their training in various universities and colleges and hospitals received much stimulus from a fresh consideration of the ancient learning of Greece and Rome, coupled with a growing desire to test out all knowledge by observation and experiment. Matters proceeded slowly during Tudor times in England; even in the days of Queen Elizabeth the diagnosis of the patient's illness was determined by physicians who inspected a flask of the patient's urine and consulted his horoscope in the stars, but they barely examined his body. God had determined the day of his death. A physician had almost no power to prolong life and he dare not shorten it.[46] Doctors were however beginning to attend the death-bed of distinguished persons; they were attempting to assuage their pains. Dying began to be a medical problem observed by the physicians.

This was the background to the writings of Sir Thomas More (1478–1535) when at the beginning of the sixteenth century he wrote about an idealized community called Utopia:

Such as be sick of incurable diseases they comfort by sitting by them, by talking with them, and, to be short, with all manner of helps that maybe. But if the disease be not only incurable, but also full of continual pain and anguish, then the priests and the magistrates exhort the man, seeing he is not able to do any duty of life, and by overliving his own death is noisome and irksome to others, and grievous to himself: that he will determine with himself no longer to cherish that pestilent and painful disease: and seeing that his life is to him but a torment, he will not be unwilling to die, but rather take a good hope to him and either despatch himself out of that painful life, as out of a prison or a rack of torment, or else suffer himself willingly to be rid out of it by other.[47]

It should be noted that doctors did not enter the picture at all either to decide if the disease was incurable or to administer the lethal drug. Death remained a matter for the priests and magistrates.

At the end of the Elizabethan era physicians had established a definite role in the care of the dying, for they could ease their pains. Doctors began to attend the bedside of many notable persons, so that Francis Bacon wrote that a physician's office was 'not only to restore health, but to mitigate pains and dolors, and not only when such mitigation may conduce to recovery, but when it may serve to make a fair and easy passage'.[48] When the whole paragraph is read in the original it seems clear that physicians were asked to alleviate the pains of dying. There was no suggestion that life should be shortened by administering a lethal drug; some have considered this passage refers to the termination of life by voluntary euthanasia[49] but have strained interpretation to signify approval of this action.

Medical knowledge increased slowly in the seventeenth and eighteenth centuries but the great advance in pathology and bacteriology occurred little over one hundred years ago. Thus there was no knowledge in the Middle Ages of a group of diseases called cancer, which receives no explicit reference in the Bible, and, except for cancer of the breast,[50] little mention in the ancient medical literature of Greece and Rome. Only very slowly as a result of the examination of tissues removed at a surgical operation or at an autopsy was it realized that a wide variety of apparently different diseases had certain common features and the concept of cancer arose. This knowledge slowly became known to the general public who regarded with dismay the possibility of contracting an incurable disease.

At the same time during the last century there was a growth of humanitarian feeling, and people found it revolting to witness any physical suffering, whether in human beings or in animals. This was part of the enlightened movement which led to the abolition of slavery, and forbad the employment of children and women under conditions of work that had disgraced the industrial revolution. Many were moving away from an implicit faith in a God who determined the day of birth and the hour of death. Death still remained an inevitable end to the chapter of life, but the question increasingly was asked whether doctors, who could now diagnose whether a man had an incurable disease, might not only ease the pains of death but also shorten the period of suffering. The climate was propitious for the modern debate on euthanasia in which the doctors would play a decisive, indeed an active part.

The modern debate

The modern debate on euthanasia started with a lively discussion in the magazine, the *Fortnightly Review*, which in 1873 carried a moving article by Tollemache, entitled somewhat cryptically 'The New Cure for Incurables',[51] in which he supported proposals concerning euthanasia made in the previous year. The *Spectator*[52] criticized these proposals, which would restrict euthanasia to those able to ask for it, but would deny it to the worst sufferers, those who were too ill to make their request known. In his reply[53] Tollemache made it clear that euthanasia must be restricted to those who asked for it; it must be on a voluntary basis. It could not apply therefore to any senile person who had lost his faculties, or to idiots who had none. The modern debate on voluntary euthanasia, for those who ask for it, had now begun.

It has been stated that the first doctor to advocate euthanasia in Britain was Dr Goddard, who proposed a scheme to the Willesden Medical Society in 1907,[54] but no details have been traced. Events moved slowly but increased sensitivity to needless pain in dying persons is reflected in the attitude to the cases of 'mercy-killing' which are mentioned below (pp. 21f). At this early stage of the debate about euthanasia there was much uncertainty about proposed methods of administration. Thus in 1928 E. A. W. Gisborne put forward the alarming suggestion that any sufferer from an incurable disease should be given a lethal dose of an opiate drug and 'there would be no need to consult the sufferer'![55] Anglican churchmen too began to reconsider their attitude. Thus Dean Inge in 1930 stated that he considered that life could be terminated if a person was suffering from a painful incurable disease, but added: 'I hope, inconsistently perhaps, that if I were attacked by a painful illness I should have patience to wait to the end.'[56] Canon Peter Green, who had much pastoral experience in Manchester, was more explicit, writing in 1931,

I should myself like my doctor, in conjunction with a specialist, to be allowed to state that the disease was fatal, and likely to be slow and painful; and then I might be permitted to make a sworn declaration that I desired to end my life at once in a painless manner.[57]

The year 1931 marked the real inauguration of the medical debate on euthanasia, for in that year Dr Killick Millard chose to give his Presidential Address to the Society of Medical Officers of Health on euthanasia, published subsequently as a book[58] together with the text of a proposed bill, the Voluntary Euthanasia (Legalisation) Bill. He asserted that 'vast numbers of human beings are doomed to end their earthly existence by a lingering, painful and often agonising form of death' and that cancer had increased much in recent years. He made a long survey of the ethics of suicide and euthanasia. He considered that suicide was to be deprecated since it was an irrevocable step and was illegal. On the other hand if voluntary euthanasia was legalized, there would then be a fundamental distinction for the latter would have become lawful. Voluntary euthanasia should be legalized for adults suffering from an 'incurable, fatal, painful disease'. Two independent medical certificates should accompany every application. The most elaborate safeguards were proposed, a magistrate attesting the application which would be submitted to an official Euthanasia referee who would be medically qualified. He would interview the applicant, then submit all the papers and attend a special Court, as would representatives of the near relatives who would be able to lodge objections. After deliberation the Court would issue a permit for euthanasia to be administered by a procedure approved by the Ministry of Health and by a specially licensed medical practitioner, in the presence of an official witness, all of whom must sign the special death certificate. The Minister of Health was to publish an official Schedule of 'incurable, fatal, painful diseases', one of which must be certified to be present in the applicant. These safeguards were extremely thorough and ironically were one of the main criticisms of the Bill when it was introduced into the House of Lords in 1936.

While some criticized Dr Millard's Presidential Address, others supported it, including some distinguished doctors. In 1935 the Euthanasia Society was formed (to become in 1969 the Voluntary Euthanasia Society). Its aim was

To create a public opinion favourable to the view that an adult person suffering severely from a fatal illness, for which no cure is known, should be entitled by law to the mercy of a painless death if and when that is his expressed wish: and to promote this legislation.

Lord Moynihan, a former President of the Royal College of Surgeons, was the first president of the Euthanasia society. He was supported by certain respected members of the public such as Sir James Jeans, the distinguished astronomer, and certain clergy such as Dean Inge, Dr Norwood (President of the Free Church Council), Dean Matthews, and certain surgeons and physicians such as Sir William Arbuthnot-Lane, Sir Humphrey Rolleston and others. In 1936 Lord Ponsonby introduced a bill into the House of Lords to legalize euthanasia; it had been modelled on the lines set forth by Dr Millard in his Presidential Address and contained numerous stringent safeguards. The bill met with much criticism, the medical peers saying that the safeguards would prove too onerous and would constitute an impossible burden for the dying man. The second reading of the bill was defeated by 35 votes to 14.[59]

It is probable that the formation of the Euthanasia Society in Great Britain was one of the reasons that prompted the formation of a comparable society in the United States in 1938 by the Rev. Charles Potter. A Bill, similar to the 1936 Euthanasia bill in Britain, was drafted but failed to secure an introduction into the New York State Assembly. It was however laid before the Nebraska Assembly in 1938 but was not passed.

At first the American Society stated that it would advocate euthanasia of infants suffering from severe physical or mental handicaps, if the parents gave permission. It dropped this suggestion in 1941 following the results of a questionnaire of American doctors. The British Euthanasia Society has never advocated the euthanasia of handicapped infants, but individuals from time to time have advocated it. Thus Lord Chorley in drawing the attention of the House of Lords in 1950 to the desirability of legislation on voluntary euthanasia, stated that it would be necessary to consider this matter eventually,[60] and the able review by Professor Glanville Williams on euthanasia in 1958 stated that there were many arguments in favour of this practice even if at present it was supported only by a small number of individuals.[61]

The compulsory destruction of many hundreds of thousands of persons by the Nazis during the Second World War brought confusion to the movement to legalize voluntary euthanasia, for this murder of unwilling persons was called euthanasia by its perpetrators. The word genocide is more appropriate, because most of them were Jews, but it should be remembered that those who were senile or psychotic and children who were severely handicapped were subjected to destruction. It must also be remembered that doctors associated themselves with these terrible happenings, acting in the name of science and in the interest of racial purity.

At the end of the war international medical organizations were moved to declare their abhorrence of these happenings in the Third Reich. The Declaration of Geneva (International Code of Medical Ethics) 1948 asked doctors to uphold this promise: 'Even under threat, I will not use my medical knowledge contrary to the laws of humanity.' The Universal Declaration of Human Rights, adopted by the General Assembly of the United Nations declared that 'Everyone has a right to life' (Article 3). The General Assembly of the World Medical Association in 1950 therefore adopted a resolution recommending that all national medical bodies 'condemn the practice of euthanasia under any circumstance', and the Council of the British Medical Association signified its agreement.

There have been various efforts to define human rights dating from the Declaration of Human Rights of the United Nations in 1948 and culminating in 1953 in a European Convention. The United Kingdom has adopted the enactments of the 1953 European Convention as legally binding; if they are infringed, individuals have the right to petition directly the Secretary-General, Council of Europe, Strasbourg.[62] Article 2 of this Convention reads:

Everyone's right to life shall be protected by law. No one shall be deprived of his life intentionally save in the execution of a sentence of a court following his conviction of a crime for which the penalty is provided by law.[63]

It is difficult to see how legislation permitting voluntary euthanasia can be passed in any of the eleven European countries who have adopted the 1953 European Convention on Human Rights, or the 1948 Declaration. Some modification would be required, a fact recognized by the 2513 supporters of voluntary euthanasia who signed and presented a petition to this effect. It was not successful. Those who support voluntary euthanasia in Britain have not, as far as I am aware, discussed this legal obstacle.

The voluntary euthanasia movement in Britain gathered strength from the publication in 1958 by Professor Glanville Williams' book, *The Sanctity of Life and the Criminal Law.* This is the most comprehensive study of modern and more tolerant attitudes to many practices such as infanticide, abortion, sterilization, suicide and euthanasia. He analysed the reasons that led to the rejection of the 1936 Euthanasia Bill. Criticism had focused on the onerous legal safeguards in that bill. Glanville Williams stated that he had every reason to believe that some doctors were already administering euthanasia to patients dying from incurable, painful disease, although strictly speaking this was illegal. He proposed that a short bill should legalize this practice.

Lord Raglan introduced the Voluntary Euthanasia Bill (see Appendix C) into the House of Lords on 25 March 1969; modelled largely along the lines suggested by Glanville Williams, it proposed to empower doctors to administer euthanasia to any adult person who had signed a declaration, witnessed by two other persons, requesting the painless induction of death. Two doctors, one being of consultant status, had to certify that the person had a serious illness or impairment reasonably thought to be incurable and expected to cause severe distress or render him incapable of rational existence. After the patient had signed the declaration requesting euthanasia a period of thirty days would elapse before administration, thereby demonstrating the determined desire of the sufferer. No doctor or nurse would be under any obligation to participate in voluntary euthanasia if they had conscientious objection.

An important new feature of the 1969 Bill lay in the provision of an advance declaration. If this declaration had been signed by an adult, and re-executed within twelve months, it would remain in force for life, unless revoked. If such a person subsequently contracted an incurable illness or incurable mental impairment, no delay of thirty days would be required before administration of euthanasia. In the original declaration the person had stated that, if he subsequently developed mental impairment deemed to be incurable and expected to cause him distress, the administration of euthanasia should be left to the discretion of his own doctor, for at that time the patient would be incapable of giving directions. Baroness

Serota, for the Ministry of Social Services (and Health), criticized the
Bill, saying that the administrative difficulties rendered the Bill
unworkable. The Bill also came under heavy censure on account of
poor drafting and vague definition of many of the terms employed.
A number of peers, however, spoke in favour of the principle of
voluntary euthanasia. Thus Lord Platt, a former President of the
Royal College of Physicians, recognized that points of criticism
might be raised, but wished to record his approval of the principle
involved. The second reading of the Bill was rejected by 61 votes to
41, but the latter registered the weight of opinion which supported
the basic principle of voluntary euthanasia.

The year 1969 saw the publication, under the Rev. Benjamin
Downing (Chairman of the Voluntary Euthanasia Society) as editor,
of *Euthanasia and the Right to Death*. The central argument of the
book concerned the right of a mature person to choose death – the
right to die – if his disease was incurable and distressing. If this right
was established it followed not only that the act should be deemed
legal, but also that the person could ask for assistance to implement
his decision for death. An authoritative number of articles by a
variety of experts set forth the ethical, legal, medical and religious
aspects of voluntary euthanasia in the light of the proposals set forth
in Lord Raglan's Bill on Voluntary Euthanasia (1969). The book
stated clearly that co-operation with the medical profession was
essential:

The co-operation of a substantial section of the medical profession in these
express and implied forms of assisted suicide require that it be open to a
patient to ask the doctor to choose a time for the giving of euthanasia that
is not known to the patient.[64]

The book also contained one comprehensive article by Professor
Yale Kamisar setting forth the legal objections to legislation on
voluntary euthanasia. He based his arguments entirely on the legal,
administrative and ethical aspects and omitted any discussion of
religious considerations. To this Professor Glanville Williams
replied.[65]

The year 1969 was significant in one other respect: in that year, for
the first time, doctors started holding professional meetings to discuss
voluntary euthanasia. Previously there had been no discussion of this
subject by professional associations of the medical profession. There
was a discussion at the Royal Society of Medicine in London on
13 October 1969.[66] Speaking as a physician, Lord Platt said that

euthanasia might be justified under certain circumstances; thus there was no justification for keeping alive a body which had suffered irrevocable brain damage, and life that was reduced to vegetable-like existence, especially if life was prolonged by mechanical procedures such as an artificial respirator. He was, however, against a blanket approval of euthanasia under too wide a category of conditions. Professor Glanville Williams, however, supported voluntary euthanasia, provided the correct safeguards were present. (As Lord Raglan's Bill had been criticized some six months previously for the inadequacy of the safeguards, it is regrettable that no details were given concerning any new proposals for adequate safeguards.) Glanville Williams said that when a doctor, under the pretext of relieving pain, gave increasing doses of morphine to a moribund patient, he knew that the patient would die of respiratory failure. If other drugs were to be discovered which relieved the pain as well as morphine but caused less respiratory depression, the doctor who used morphine in this manner might lay himself open to a prosecution for murder. In these circumstances doctors might want euthanasia legalized. He felt that legislation was needed to allow patients who were severely ill, unlikely to recover, and in acute pain, to be offered euthanasia. On the other hand he considered that many elderly people would regard voluntary euthanasia with considerable apprehension; they might even be induced to agree to it, or even to volunteer, but for the wrong motives.

A comparable discussion, but without any new facts emerging, took place in November 1969 under the joint auspices of the Royal College of General Practitioners and the Institute of Religion and Medicine.[67] At neither of these meetings were details given of categories of patients for whom voluntary euthanasia was permissible and those to be excluded. There was no discussion of what were the right motives which would lead an elderly person to choose euthanasia: thus is the natural but self-centred desire to avoid pain an acceptable motive, but the unselfish desire to stop being a burden an unacceptable motive? Who decides what is right and what is wrong in motivation? Who can, in any case, probe motives? These are some of the unanswered questions which will be raised in this book. It is not so much that these questions are never answered; they are never asked, as concrete questions demanding a concrete answer by a doctor or by a person who debates 'to be or not to be'.

The Representative Body of the British Medical Association in

1969 passed a resolution, confirming the policy declared first in 1950, that the medical profession had a duty to preserve life and to relieve pain, but it condemned euthanasia. It asked its Council to give this view publicity. The Board of Science and Education appointed a panel of ten doctors to consider the problem of euthanasia. They received evidence from members, medical and lay, of the Voluntary Euthanasia Society. Their report (1971), printed below as Appendix A, unanimously condemned voluntary euthanasia; it considered that existing medical practice could ensure adequate control of pain in almost all terminal cases. It stressed the inadequate facilities for the care of the dying. It suggested that some medical schools might have neglected teaching and research in this important field. It considered that legislation for voluntary euthanasia could never contain adequate safeguards. Further, there would always be some errors in medical diagnosis and prognosis. The panel of BMA doctors, of which I had the honour to be Chairman, confined its attention to medical aspects of voluntary euthanasia and avoided discussion of the legal, moral and religious issues. It is not always recognized that the twin aims of the medical profession, namely the relief of suffering and the preservation of life, may at times be incompatible. In those dying from painful conditions, it was admitted that slight risk of respiratory depression might occur with the high dosage of drugs required to control pain in terminal states. The report considered that it was justifiable for doctors to take this risk in treating an incurable painful disease, even increasing the drugs to produce periods of stupor or unconsciousness if the pain was very severe. This does not constitute what is understood as 'voluntary euthanasia'.

The report was received favourably in the press. Important criticism came from the journal *Nature*,[68] which stated that a substantial number of elderly and chronic sick did not want to live, although they suffered no physical pain and the BMA report had not discussed whether these persons had a 'right to die'. *New Society*[69] stated that there was an area, as when a person was in an artificial respirator, in which doctors did make life-and-death decisions, and that it was impossible for them to avoid these issues. Another example concerned decisions about who should receive renal dialysis, when everyone could not be offered treatment by this expensive machine. It suggested that the BMA report had shelved these issues.

The *New Statesman*[70] took exception to the assertion in the BMA report that it was considered that few doctors were deliberately terminating the life of incurable patients. The writer in this journal stated:

I am deeply and thankfully convinced that euthanasia in the proper sense of the word has for long been practised quite widely in this country, with compassion, with wisdom, and free of the horrors that would surround such an act done according to the terms and conditions of some law. And that is why I believe we should leave well alone.

That, to my mind, is the central issue in *legislation* on voluntary euthanasia, although other unanswered questions, like that of lonely elderly people who do not want to live, must also receive sympathetic consideration.

Reference, however brief, must be made to the subject of 'mercy-killings', that is, the killing of a person, adult or child, by another person, usually a member of the same family, from motives of compassion. These cases usually receive considerable publicity in the press. The overwhelming number of mercy-killings have occurred without the consent of the victim, or the person killed was a child, so that these are examples of involuntary euthanasia. They will therefore not be discussed in detail in this book.

The most notorious alleged mercy-killings have occurred in the United States. Thus a Dr H. N. Sander was charged with the mercy-killing of a cancer-patient, but was acquitted. He had admitted injecting air intravenously to a patient who was *in extremis*, but subsequently defended himself by saying that the person was already dead. The patient probably was dead, or so nearly so as to make no difference, and he was certainly incapable of giving permission for euthanasia. The family were bitterly divided over the issue, the husband and one brother supporting the doctor, another brother bitterly opposed.[71] Another notorious case of mercy-killing from the United States is barely relevant to the discussion of voluntary euthanasia. Miss Carol Ana Paight, who had a cancer phobia, shot her father, who was unconscious and recovering from the anaesthetic given during an operation at which cancer of the stomach was found.[72]

In Britain some of the most famous mercy-killings have elicited public sympathy, but all of them were examples of involuntary euthanasia. In 1915 a young soldier called Simpson was found guilty of the murder of his severely ill child.[73] He was under great emotional strain: on leave, and waiting for his unfaithful wife to return to the neglected sick child. In 1927 a man drowned his seriously ill child, suffering from tuberculosis and gangrene of the face. He had been sitting up with her all night. The judge in his summing-up recommended mercy and the jury returned a verdict of not guilty of murder.[74] In 1934 another mercy-killer was reprieved in England. A woman was charged with the murder of her 31-year-old imbecile son. She was distraught not knowing who would look after the imbecile when she went into hospital for a big operation. Although condemned for murder she was reprieved two days later.[75] In 1946 an overwrought father gassed his deformed imbecile daughter. He was found guilty of murder, but the sentence was commuted to life imprisonment.[76]

These cases are set forth in some detail as examples of 'mercy-killing' because there has been some confusion in the popular mind between mercy-killing and euthanasia. The Royal Commission on Capital Punishment of 1953 had difficulty in making a firm definition of mercy-killing; it could cite only examples such as 'where a mother has killed her child or a husband has killed his wife from merciful motives of pity and humanity'. Evidence given to the Commission stressed the pathos of those cases, some of which have just been mentioned, but 'it was agreed by almost all witnesses' that it would 'often prove extremely difficult to distinguish killings where the motive was merciful from those where it was not'.[77] The Commission therefore 'reluctantly' concluded that 'it would not be possible' to frame and apply a satisfactory definition to cover all cases.[78] It therefore could not exempt mercy-killing from the current law of murder.

In 1927 Mr Justice Branson, while summing up in one of the cases just mentioned, said:

It is a matter which gives food for thought when one comes to consider that, had this poor child been an animal instead of a human being, so far from there being anything blameworthy in the man's action in putting an end to its suffering, he would actually have been liable to punishment if he had not done so.[79]

These memorable words, quoted throughout the euthanasia literature, certainly provoke thought. They suggest one cogent reason for euthanasia, but they omit to state that an animal is a different category of being, however lovable. An animal is owned, it may be sold, or killed, it cannot ask for euthanasia, or object to it. An owner may have his bitch spayed to prevent mating; he cannot solve adolescent tantrums in his daughter in the same manner. A parent does not own his child.

II

The Case for Legislation

This chapter represents some of the views expressed by the supporters of legislation on voluntary euthanasia, but is not to be
regarded as a comprehensive statement. It does *not* represent the
views of the author of the present book.

During the present century a more liberal attitude has been adopted
in Western society towards many matters which had been regarded as
taboo and sinful. Capital punishment is no longer meted out to the
murderer; he requires rational scientific investigation by a psychiatrist, to be followed by the appropriate treatment as well as suitable
punishment. Male homosexuality between consenting adults is no
longer regarded as a crime, although it may be a deviation from the
normal pattern of heterosexuality. Suicide is no longer regarded as a
criminal act. It may be the symptom of mental depression, which can
be treated by a psychiatrist. Possibly it is a natural reaction to intolerable misery and deserves compassion. Since suicide has ceased to be
a felony, or even a crime, many regard it as a legal anomaly that it
should be a punishable offence to aid and abet suicide out of compassionate and altruistic motives. Indeed it may be argued that the
Suicide Act (1961) has recognized a man's right to decide his own
death.

Birth control has become widely acceptable. Indeed it is essential
in order to avoid having too many children in a family, too many
citizens in one state. World-overpopulation is a very serious threat.
Just as modern man has found it necessary to control the processes of
birth so it will prove necessary to control the factors which determine
death. Our ability to prolong life adds urgently to the problem of
death control. Human birth and death can no longer be left to the
blind forces of nature.

The present chapter is therefore written to present the arguments
in favour of voluntary euthanasia for an adult person suffering from
an incurable distressing disorder. It will not be possible for the reader

to make up his mind whether to support legislation concerning voluntary euthanasia unless he examines the arguments set forth by the Voluntary Euthanasia Society of Great Britain,[1] and authoritative books on this subject.[2]

The main arguments for voluntary euthanasia are compassion towards others and the assertion of the right, as far as the medical situation is concerned, to determine the time of one's own death. It is natural for people to hope that, when the time comes, they will die peacefully, without prolonged suffering and with dignity. Those who do will be fortunate, for many are compelled to endure a long-drawn-out and deeply distressing process of dying.

Compassion insists that sufferers should be free to decide whether they wish their lives to end without great and prolonged suffering, which is a trial not only for the patient but also for the relatives. It must of course be a completely voluntary act on the part of the sufferer, the expression of a steady and sanely determined wish of the patient. That is the reason for the delay of thirty days suggested in the Voluntary Euthanasia Bill (1969) between the application for euthanasia and its administration. At any time during this period, the application for voluntary euthanasia can be revoked. The voluntary principle is also extended to doctors and nurses, none of whom should be under any compulsion to participate; if any of them have conscientious objections these will be respected. The Voluntary Euthanasia Society considers that a significant proportion of doctors would co-operate if the necessary legislation was enacted. Doctors and nurses would be in a position to opt out of a euthanasia situation if their scruples so demanded. For the suffering patient the request for euthanasia is regarded as a natural human right.

Each year nearly 600,000 die in England and Wales. Of these nearly 50% die of diseases of the heart or the blood vessels of the brain, 20% from cancer or some other malignant disease, 20% from diseases of the lungs. Much has been done to reduce deaths in childhood, but these were usually the swift, merciful deaths of infection. Nowadays a baby boy in England can expect to live until 68, a baby girl until 74.[3]

Although young adults, and those in the prime of life, are less frequently attacked by mortal illness, yet they may have complaints that last longer and cause more physical distress than those of the elderly. If their complaint is incurable, and to them unendurable, and especially if it is likely to prove fatal, these young or middle-aged adults should be allowed the choice of dying painlessly, and be allowed any necessary medical assistance to that end. It is quite wrong to envisage voluntary euthanasia as an option only for the aged; it is a choice that any responsible adult should be able to make, provided he is physically incapacitated by disease and suffering, and unable therefore to bring about his own death. Observations have been made on the degree of pain sustained by hospital patients of various ages during the course of a fatal illness. Of those under 50 years old, 45% had considerable discomfort; 32% of those between 50 and 70 had moderate pain and only 10% of those over 70 years had much unrelieved pain during their last illness.[4]

Cancer is perhaps the most dreaded of all the incurable disorders. Complete permanent cures do occur especially in certain varieties of malignant disease. Those who report early to their doctors stand a better chance of obtaining a complete cure; even when this does not occur, many years may elapse before there is any return of the disease. This may be in a mild form and amenable to therapy.

Too often the disease is found eventually to affect many parts of the body. In the end there may come a stage when cure is no longer hoped for, even by the doctor, so that its slow implacable course is much dreaded. It is true that pain is variable, even in the same variety of cancer, for it depends much on which structures are involved. Pressure on nerves or deposits in bone may be very painful. It is often stated that only a quarter of those patients who are dying of cancer have pain, but some of these have severe pain, so that taking the mortality statistics into account there must be a considerable amount of suffering.

There are some special institutions in which even the severe pain of the terminal stage of cancer can be well relieved.[5] Relief is then possible in some 97–99% of patients. This signifies that almost all can be relieved, except some in whom psychological pain is the main factor. This point is accepted by those who support voluntary euthanasia but they point out that these special institutions are costly affairs, that they have many staff in comparison to the number of patients. Everyone on the staff has been highly trained in this speciality, that is, the control of severe pain in terminal illness. Many of the staff have chosen to work in these institutions as a personal expression of their dedication to this task. Medicines and tablets by mouth, likewise injections and other treatments, can be administered with absolute regularity, almost to the minute, at very frequent intervals, say every four hours, so that the patient comes to rely on them. He knows that he will receive another injection before the pain returns in any severe degree.[6]

Treatment also can be very effective in many other hospitals, but it is difficult to block a bed in one of the largest hospitals, especially if it is a teaching hospital, for many weeks, or even months, before the terminal cancer patient has died. Patients therefore tend to be accommodated in a variety of hospitals designed to accommodate long-stay patients. In any hospital apart from the specialized institutions those dying of cancer probably represent only a small proportion of the total number of those who are seriously ill in the same ward. In treatment they have to take their turn. Possibly many of the staff do not claim to have had special training in the control of severe pain in the terminal stages of cancer. The prescribing of the narcotic and analgesic drugs may be left to junior members of the medical or surgical staff. If pain is not adequately controlled this may be because there is less experience of alternative narcotic drugs, or combinations of drugs, say a narcotic drug and a tranquilliser in the correct dosage, than is found among the staff of a specialized institution. Possibly relief would be obtained if the narcotics were given at frequent intervals, but shortages of staff and the needs of other patients may make it difficult to ensure the punctuality of administration that is such a feature of the specialized unit. It is this regularity of administration in adequate dosage that contributes so much to the confidence of the patient. It is hardly to be expected that the medical and nursing staff of a general ward can devote as much time to the psychological and other needs of someone dying of cancer as occurs in special units devoted to this task. Thus Professor Hinton,[7] surveying patients in a general hospital, found that 12% of those dying of incurable disease had pain which was inadequately relieved.

More than half the deaths in Great Britain occur outside hospital. While it is true that every effort is made by medical practitioners to secure admission to hospital of any cancer patient who is having much pain in the last stage of his illness, it is not always possible to secure a bed and a certain proportion of patients choose to remain and die at home. Matters may not be as unsatisfactory as they were some twenty years ago when a survey was made of the work of district nurses in the care of some 7,000 cancer patients who died at home. They found over half the patients had moderate or severe suffering.[8] This was a very disturbing report. More recently, in 1959, the families of those who had died of a cancer at home were questioned and some 20% of the relatives gave distressing descriptions of severe unrelieved pain.[9] In 1965 another survey of cancer patients who died at home found that some 8% had severe pain, inadequately controlled, and this lasted for more than three months.[10] The fall from 50% some twenty years ago to 20% seven years later and then to 8% is encouraging, but it cannot be taken as completely accurate. For one thing it is impossible for pain to be measured either by the sufferer or by the observer. All that can be said is that there is much to suggest that there is improved care of cancer patients who die at home, but that one in ten or even more have severe pain which is not well controlled.

Diseases of the heart and blood-vessels are actually the commonest cause of death. This may occur painlessly when a person has a fatal stroke. Others survive the stroke, they may even make a complete recovery, but a proportion are left paralysed, even speechless. These may survive for many years before another stroke or some infection carries them off. A heart attack can be fatal and the pain although severe is well controlled by an injection, but other attacks may occur. Angina is another possibility with short attacks of severe pain, often eased by a tablet under the tongue. If the heart itself is showing signs of failure difficult breathing may be severe and not easily relieved. Weakness may be severe and nausea may occur.

Diseases of the chest may result in difficult breathing; this may be most distressing and difficult to relieve. Cough can be very troublesome.

There are other diseases, which although not common, may cause progressive paralysis or some other manifestation of a disordered function of the nervous system. As these diseases seldom directly threaten life, the patient may have to endure the illness for many years. In the end he may be unable to feed himself, turn the pages of a book, or even speak. Motor car accidents may affect the spine, sometimes leaving paralysis in both legs and bladder trouble for life. If the neck is broken a few survive, possibly completely paralysed in all four limbs for many years, until death appears as a merciful release. All these long-standing neurological conditions are grievous and frustrating in the extreme for the sufferer; they are also extremely distressing for the relatives.

It is well known that elderly persons may lose their faculties, even become demented. They may become dirty in their beds and their feeding; they may fail to recognize their families. Their existence can be described as animal, even vegetable. A person may change until he is only a travesty of his former self. He cannot die with human dignity. Friends and relatives feel much distress at seeing all this. This condition is much feared by middle-aged persons who see the complete destruction of someone they loved and respected. They fear that this might happen to them and that, when demented, they will not be able to ask for a merciful termination. To provide for this contingency, the Voluntary Euthanasia Society has advocated an advance declaration, a matter to be explained subsequently.

It seems ironical that some of the achievements of modern surgery and medicine can prolong at times the act of dying. The use of a mechanical respirator after a head injury may save many lives which would have been lost only a few decades ago. But not all recover; a small proportion recover only partially and are paralysed or have grave reduction of their mental functions for the remainder of their lives. If the quality of mental life is negligible it may be asked whether it is kind to keep this shell alive. Other methods of resuscitation are used for those who have heart attacks, and these may be justified when the person is in the prime of life but are perhaps less desirable in those who are elderly. Much, often unfairly, depends on the individual judgment of the attending doctor who may or may not be attentive to the more human and non-medical considerations or the known wishes of his patient in the matter of dying.

At times operations are planned as emergency measures, not only on those who have a good chance of recovery, but on those who have some fatal disease such as cancer. Operations may leave patients with unnatural orifices through which the bowels empty themselves or urine is passed. Other persons when seriously ill have tubes inserted at various sites, through which fluids pass into the body; in others various machines remove the secretions from the throat or some other part of the body. Electrical currents can be passed into the heart to control its contractions. Visitors to units of intensive care see all this technological machinery operating on a man; sometimes he recovers but at other times the relatives must ask why the doctors do not just let the patient die. Doctors who feel that they must preserve life at all costs have however only one duty: they must prolong life, cost what it may to their patient. (Whether indeed this does constitute the duty of a doctor to a dying person is discussed on pp. 43 f. below.)

It is not proposed to continue the catalogue. Every new discovery in medical and surgical science will have its triumphs, but there will also be the harmful fall-out. It is not proposed to publish here any of the numerous letters received by the Voluntary Euthanasia Society on behalf of those dying slowly and with distress. One alone may be referred to, since it was reported in a medical journal, in a letter headed 'Not allowed to die.'[11] It has been quoted in the 1970 brochure of the Voluntary Euthanasia Society. It told of a deceased doctor who had retired after coronary thrombosis and developed cancer of the stomach. An operation was performed to deal with the cancer but it had spread far and wide. Part of the stomach was removed and the diagnosis was confirmed. Analgesic drugs to deaden pain and even morphine injections at night only partially controlled the pain, as the growths had spread to the spine and were pressing on the nerves. Ten days after the operation a clot of blood suddenly blocked one of the arteries of the lungs. This might have proved rapidly fatal had not an emergency operation removed the clot. The patient expressed his appreciation of the good intentions and skills of the young surgeon but asked that if other complications occurred no steps should be taken to prolong his life. He wrote a note to this effect on his case records. Two weeks later he had another coronary thrombosis but was resuscitated by the hospital's emergency team. That night his heart stopped four times; each time it was re-started artificially. He lingered on for three more weeks, but, perhaps fortunately for him, his brain was not functioning and he was unconscious. Intravenous fluids however fed him and antibiotics prevented infections. On the last day plans were made to help his failing breathing by an artificial respirator but the heart stopped before this endeavour could be realized. This terrible letter, written by a doctor, concluded: 'This case report is submitted for publication without commentary or conclusions.'

It should be added that this case of malpractice did not occur in Britain. However such occurrences take place here, as shown by the comment in a letter from Dr W. Ritchie Russell of the United Oxford Hospitals in a later number of the same journal.[12]

Professor W. St C. Symmers gives a horrifying account of the infliction of unnecessary suffering by prolonging the existence of a dying patient. This is an extreme example of what may be observed in the wards of every hospital in the country, and it is important to realize that many are coming to look on this sort of thing as a type of malpractice which is bringing discredit to both the medical and nursing professions.

The grounds for the legalization of voluntary euthanasia do not rest on a rare case of manifest malpractice but on what is commonly happening in the terminal care of dying patients. Thus Professor Hinton visited during the last and fatal illness patients in a general hospital in London in recent years and has written:

Two-thirds were liable to experience pain which required treatment for its relief . . . Unfortunately regular visits and reports of these dying people could only confirm that in some the failure to achieve adequate relief of pain did persist. In those who remained conscious (unconsciousness mercifully protects many from suffering towards the end of life) about one person in eight continued to have pain for some part of the day. At times they had a mild degree of discomfort that did not trouble them much, but it was likely to get really painful at other times. A few were very rarely free of pain, although it had been dulled. This proportion of about one chance in eight of experiencing pain in the terminal illness seems to be a fair generalization from the various sources. It seems to be more common than it should be.[13]

Voluntary euthanasia rests on a basic human right – the right to die, if death is the only release from suffering. A responsible man, faced with the prospect of pain, disability and death has a right to choose a merciful release and to have medical assistance if this is necessary. Surely it will be but an act of compassion to assist him in this action, if he is helpless and if his desire is a considered, deliberate one evinced over a period of a few weeks, say one month, as suggested in Lord Raglan's Voluntary Euthanasia Bill (1969).

The right to die has been argued forcibly by many people. Its ethical and religious basis has been argued by Professor Joseph Fletcher, formerly of the Episcopal (Anglican) Theological College, Cambridge, Massachusetts.[14] He has pointed out that the supreme commandment is 'Love thy neighbour.' This contains all that is needed. In every new situation the Christian must ask how love of the neighbour shows itself. One does not ask for rules about right or wrong, or even moral absolutes, enshrined in a legal code forbidding always and at all places actions such as stealing, lying or killing. There are exceptions to every rule, exceptions dictated by the law of love. No one would condemn a pauper who, dying of hunger, stole a crust of bread. No one would condemn a mother who told a lie to guard her child from a criminal lunatic. No one would condemn a girl who defended her life and her virtue with a poker, even if the ruffian sustained a fractured skull. If there are these exceptions, are there not other exceptions, when it would be a mercy to allow someone dying a slow painful death to take poison – or even to kill himself by starving to death, as occurred in the Roman empire?

Fletcher has recently defended his point of view,[15] saying that there are only three methods by which moral decisions can be made. First there is determination by absolute values enshrined in commandments and legal codes. Secondly, there is the application of love for the neighbour in every new situation, that is, 'situation ethics'. Thirdly, there is the refusal to discuss moral values; those who take this line just discuss various plans in terms which take no cognizance of ethics, as that term is usually understood. They often invoke common sense.

Using these criteria Fletcher has pointed to the inconsistencies in the action of doctors. They may practise *direct euthanasia* – a deliberate action to shorten or to end life. A doctor, on finding that a diabetic patient has developed advanced inoperable cancer, may shorten life by advising that the insulin injections be stopped. He may end life by giving a lethal dose of morphine. Alternatively, *indirect euthanasia* may be practised by the doctor. Thus a person who is very severely paralysed may get pneumonia and the doctor may decide not to give an antibiotic. An elderly person may get a coronary attack, and the doctor may forbid any resuscitation. Viewed thus almost all doctors are performing 'indirect euthanasia', whilst some are resorting to direct euthanasia. If this contravenes existing laws of homicide and suicide, would it not be better to amend the legislation to afford protection for the doctor and the patient?

While it is true that many of the churches officially oppose voluntary euthanasia, nevertheless some religious persons have supported it. Other pronouncements even by the most influential churchmen have begun to hint at a few exceptions to the traditional rule that life be extended as long as possible. Pope Pius XII before an international audience of physicians made it clear that when the patient was in the extreme terminal stages and death was almost within sight, then physicians could desist in order to permit the patient, already virtually dead, to pass in peace. Lord Lang, Archbishop of Canterbury, in the debate on the Euthanasia Bill 1936, conceded that 'cases arise in which some means of shortening life may be justified'.[16]

It is true that the official pronouncements of the Roman Catholic Church forcibly condemn voluntary euthanasia and the pronouncements of the Anglican Church are cast clearly against any legislation.[17] Individual church leaders have expressed their convictions.

Dr Leslie Weatherhead, the distinguished Free Church minister, has written,

I sincerely believe that those who come after us will wonder why on earth we kept a human being alive against his own will, when all the dignity, beauty and meaning of life had vanished: when any gain to anyone was clearly impossible, and when we should have been punished by the State if we had kept an animal alive in similar physical conditions.[18]

Other voices have been raised in favour of voluntary euthanasia. Dean Inge, an Anglican, said, 'I do not think we can assume that God willed the prolongation of torture for the benefit of the soul of the sufferer.'[19] Canon Peter Green, from his long pastoral experience as an Anglican parish priest in Manchester, was most explicit. If his own doctor had told him that he had a fatal complaint, which would be slow and painful, and a specialist confirmed this fact, then he felt he should be able to make a sworn declaration and end his own life in some painless manner.[20] Individual Christians are therefore free to make up their own mind, whatever the official teaching of their church – this would be the point of view of the Voluntary Euthanasia Society.

Many there are who would prefer to leave theology and traditional ethics out of this question of voluntary euthanasia. Some of these feel, however, that death should be 'natural', possibly as a kind of protest against the pressures of living in a technological society. However, we do all sorts of things to dying persons to improve their lot, giving them purified tap water to drink, to say nothing of pasteurized milk, lighting the room with electric light, and telephoning relatives to request a visit. None of these things are 'natural'. Man has tamed nature. Man, the maker, has to decide whether to insert a cardiac pace-maker, to give or not to give an antibiotic, to administer or not to administer a drug in order to suppress pain. Intelligent beings must exercise their responsibility in controlling nature as far as possible. Those who support voluntary euthanasia would say that man has a right, in certain circumstances, to decide the manner and the time of his dying. They argue that their case has increasing urgency in an era of refined medical technology such as that in which we now live.

Man's power to control nature, his capacity to prolong life even when it is only a shell that remains alive, his skill in providing artificial means such as respirators, kidney-machines and pace-makers to the heart, emphasize that, whether we like it or not, decisions about death are being taken by the medical profession. Those who support voluntary euthanasia consider that the time has come to require doctors legally to take account of the wishes of their patients in determining the end of their lives and the management of their deaths. No longer, they argue, can it be accepted that only the doctor 'knows best'.

III

Legal and Ethical Aspects

If it is proposed to legalize voluntary euthanasia it is essential to understand the present state of the law, not only on the books, but in practice. The books are clear.

It is indisputably clear in the law that acting to terminate life is first degree murder. This is true regardless of the motives of the actor. At one time in the evolution of the common law of murder it might have made a difference whether a man was moved by emotions of spite or by emotions of mercy. One speaks of the element of 'malice' in the common law definition of murder. Surely a man does not kill maliciously if he kills in order to save another man from unbearable suffering. But the concept of 'malice' lost its force in the evolution of the common law as early as the sixteenth and seventeenth centuries, it came to mean nothing more significant than the requirement that the killing be intentional. Since a man killing for reasons of mercy does indeed kill intentionally, he kills maliciously, at least according to the special dictionary of the law.[1]

This was the considered statement of a professor of law at the University of Washington. He spoke for the common law of England and the United States of America.

In England, Professor Glanville Williams has summarized the position.

Under the present law, voluntary euthanasia would, except in certain narrow circumstances, be regarded as suicide in the patient who consents and murder in the doctor who administers; even on a lenient view, most lawyers would say it could not be less than manslaughter in the doctor, the punishment for which, according to the jurisdiction and the degree of manslaughter, can be anything up to imprisonment for life.[2]

If the doctor gave the fatal injection, the doctor was a murderer, for his hand committed the deed. It would be no defence that the patient consented, that his sufferings were severe, or that death from natural causes was imminent. Glanville Williams suggested however that if any doctor was tried for this offence, then the judge might direct the jury to be merciful on the general legal doctrine of necessity.[3] That is to say, the dying patient was in a pitiful state of pain and agony, uncontrolled by narcotics and sedatives administered in the usual manner; and a consultant had diagnosed an incurable fatal distressing disease, and the relatives and friends were much upset. Even laymen would understand the utter necessity to increase the dose of narcotic and sedative drugs in this patient, even if this involved a possible risk of shortening life. It was this ancient legal doctrine of necessity, that the learned judge in the famous abortion case of *Rex v. Bourne* expounded to the jury and suggested that the consultant gynaecologist might be exonerated. The circumstances of the pregnancy were pitiful in the extreme, for a young girl had been raped repeatedly.

An alternative defence could also be provided under the legal doctrine of causality. To any ordinary Englishman, who sits on any jury this means: what do you think caused the death? This legal doctrine of causality was expounded in 1957 by Mr Justice Devlin in the prosecution of Dr Bodkin Adams for the murder of one of his patients by large doses of narcotic drugs. The judge said:

No act is murder which does not cause death. 'Cause' means nothing philosophical or technical or scientific. It means what you twelve men and women sitting as a jury in the jury box would regard in a common-sense way as the cause ... If, for example, because a doctor has done something or has omitted to do something death occurs, it can be scientifically proved – if it could – at eleven o'clock instead of twelve o'clock, or even on Monday instead of Tuesday, no people of common sense would say, 'Oh, the doctor caused her death.' They would say that the cause of her death was the illness or the injury, or whatever it was, which brought her into hospital, and the proper medical treatment that is administered and that has an incidental effect of determining the exact moment of death, or may have, is not the cause of death in any sensible use of the word. But it remains the fact, and it remains the law, that no doctor, nor any man, no more in the case of the dying than of the healthy, has the right deliberately to cut the thread of life.[4]

Eminent legal opinion would maintain that there may still be uncertainty about the law as it concerns the use of narcotic drugs which in very high dosage may shorten the life of a patient. (As is pointed out on p. 83 below, narcotic drugs administered shortly before death often slightly lengthen life because they relieve distress.) Any deliberate, planned, substantial shortening of a patient's life could be regarded as murder. Thus if someone had a recurrence of cancer, but was expected to live several months, and a narcotic drug was given, either as a single large lethal injection, or in large cumulative doses, or in very rapidly rising doses (the amounts given being far in excess of that required to control the pain in this particular patient), so that as a result of the large amount of drugs the patient died within a few hours or days, the charge could be one of murder. Much would depend on whether a smaller dosage of the narcotic drug in this particular patient would have controlled the pain. If the smaller dose controlled the pain, why was the much larger dose of narcotic given?

On the other hand, if a patient was being treated by narcotic drugs, given in gradually increased dosage in order to control the pain in a fatal complaint, and any shortening of life was problematical, expectation of life being already short in duration, then the judge could direct the jury to exonerate the doctor, even in the unlikely event of any charge ever being brought. The important point would be that the dose was increased gradually in order to relieve the pain, and that no ulterior motive, such as financial gain, was also present.

Even if this deliberate termination of the life of a patient occurred, Glanville Williams[5] has pointed out how difficult it would be to establish a charge against the general medical practitioner who was attending the patient in his own home, especially if the doctor administered all the treatment, and the patient had become so seriously ill that death was anticipated by the relatives. Matters would be facilitated if it was realized that the relatives hoped that a merciful release would come soon. Even if details concerning dosage were forthcoming, it might be very difficult to prove how far this amount of the narcotic drug, rather than the disease, contributed to the fatality. There would be the added difficulty that the patient might have become habituated to the narcotic drug, so that, say, double the dose had only the same effect as the normal dose on both the pain and the failing respirations. The police would probably be loath to initiate proceedings against a doctor if it was known that the deceased had been dying of a painful, incurable complaint, especially if the doctor was held in high esteem by the neighbourhood. Most juries would acquit whatever the judge might direct about the 'law on the books'. In such a case, too, the legal doctrine of necessity might be pleaded as an extenuating circumstance.

The difficulty of establishing any charge against a medical practitioner were exemplified in 1957 when Dr John Bodkin Adams was
charged with the murder of an elderly widow aged 81 years.[6] He was
charged with administering to her in 1950 excessively large doses of
morphine and heroin, as well as other sedatives, and having intended
to kill her.

How heavily the scales were weighted against him was disclosed
when, s ubsequent to his acquittal for murder of the widow, he was
almost immediately charged and pleaded guilty to fifteen charges in
respect of other patients under the Dangerous Drugs Act, Cremation
Act, Forgery Act and Larceny Acts. At this second trial the judge
stated that the most serious of the fifteen offences concerned his
failure to record on certain cremation certificates the fact that he
knew that he would inherit money after the decease of the patient.
This omission had occurred in relation to three of his patients. (It is a
legal requirement for obvious reasons that a doctor signing a cremation certificate should not be a party to any financial gain by reason
of the death of his patient.)

The same charge had been brought against Dr Adams previously
during the trial for murder, namely his failure to record on the cremation certificate the fact that he knew he would inherit property from
the deceased widow. The fact that when she altered her will in favour
of Dr Adams she was already a drug addict, and utterly dependent on
him, added a sinister light to the question of financial gain by the
doctor. Eventually he did not inherit as much as had been expected,
in fact only a few hundred pounds, and the meagre sum told heavily
in his favour when the judge in his summing-up weighed up the question of motivation. A charge of murder involves an intention to kill
and intention presupposes that some advantage will be gained. Would
any doctor murder a person for a few hundred pounds?

In June 1948 this elderly widow had a left-sided stroke and was
admitted to a nursing home in Chester. A few days later, she had
severe pain, an unusual feature to occur in a stroke. A Chester doctor
regrettably prescribed morphine, a most unusual narcotic drug to
employ in a chronic complaint such as a stroke. The injections were
continued until some two weeks later she was transferred to a nursing
home in Eastbourne and came under the care of Dr Adams. Most
doctors, fearing the creation of addiction to morphine, would have
endeavoured to wean her from this narcotic drug. Addiction is seldom
definite under three weeks of daily treatment by morphine injections.

This drug was however continued for another two weeks and then heroin, an even more powerful narcotic, was added by Dr Adams.

Both narcotic drugs, morphine and heroin, were continued as daily injections, but remained low in dosage until the summer of 1950, a period of two years. Long before this time addiction would have become severe and it would be extremely difficult to withdraw the drug or even to hold the dosage at a moderate level.

From the summer of 1950 the dose of both drugs rose slowly, but during 7–12 November the dose rose very rapidly, being double that given in any previous period of 24 hours. On 7–9 November during each period of 24 hours 1·5 grams of morphine (22½ grains) and 1·0 gram of heroin (14½ grains) were given. On 10–12 November the daily amount of heroin increased to 1·6 grams (24½ grains), but that of morphine fell slightly to 1·2 grams (18 grains). On the last two days a new sedative, paraldehyde, was given, 5 ml. on two separate occasions.

Obviously the woman had become addicted to morphine for over two years. There was no enquiry about how this lamentable state of affairs arose, or any suggestion that it had been deliberately provoked in order that the elderly widow should become too dependent on the doctor who controlled the narcotic drug. The main point at issue in the charge of murder was the sudden doubling of the dose of both narcotic drugs between 7 and 12 November, and the administration of an injection of paraldehyde in double the normal dosage. One eminent consultant stated that in his opinion the only possible explanation of the increase of all drugs in the period 7–12 November was an intention to kill. Another doctor stated there was no clear evidence on this point: the massive increase in drugs might have been the only way to control the behaviour of someone severely addicted to both narcotic drugs. There had been no post-mortem examination; had this occurred it would have proved possible to assess approximately the amount of narcotics given. In the absence of a post-mortem examination it was impossible to prove that death had not been due to natural causes, such as pneumonia or another stroke. It was agreed by both doctors that it is impossible to state what is the fatal dose of a narcotic drug in someone who has become habituated to this narcotic drug. It should be remembered that the trial occurred some seven years after the death of the widow and occurred only when other investigations into other suspicious occurrences had taken place.

In his summing-up Mr Justice Devlin remarked that the trial was almost unique in that the question of murder had to be decided by evidence produced and interpreted by medical experts. He warned the jury that no one 'has the right to cut off life', but he also expounded the legal doctrine of causality (quoted above). Had the increased amounts of narcotics and sedatives given in the last six days of life 'caused' the death, or was death due to the incurable condition of the stroke, the prolonged period of drug addiction, complicated possibly by a terminal pneumonia? In commenting on this question of causality Glanville Williams[7] stated that he would have preferred to suggest exoneration under the legal doctrine of necessity, but he failed to amplify his point. Did he suggest that Dr Adams was under a necessity during the last six days of the widow's life to double the dose of narcotic drugs to control the behaviour of someone severely addicted to morphine and heroin? Pain was not present. The plea of necessity would have been stronger had it occurred in the treatment of someone dying of an incurable progressive disease such as cancer. Whatever our views about euthanasia, it is certain that the case of Dr Adams demonstrated the difficulties that arise in proving that death has been caused by injections of narcotic drugs and sedatives. This, of course, does not close the issue of voluntary euthanasia; there is the question of the consent of the patient, the approval of the relatives, the conscience of the doctor and the question of safeguards, all of which are discussed later in this book.[8]

Throughout the history of law a fundamental distinction has been made between acts and omissions, even if death results.[9] If a doctor supplies lethal drugs to a patient who asks to commit suicide, this act abets suicide. If a doctor administers a lethal injection to a patient, this is an act that leads to death. If a patient, who is suffering from advanced widespread incurable cancer, gets pneumonia, and the doctor decides not to give an antibiotic, this is an omission. The omission may contribute to the death of the patient; had he been given the antibiotic he might have recovered from the pneumonia. Glanville Williams[10] suggested that such a doctor, if he were charged, would probably be exempted from the alleged results of any act of omission if life had been a grievous burden to the patient, by reason of the senility of old age or inoperable widespread cancer, to give obvious examples. This view was expounded by the BMA report on *The Problem of Euthanasia*:

When a doctor is treating a patient during the last stages of illness and death is inevitable, an intercurrent infection may arise. The relevant treatment then can only be to relieve distress. It is a matter of clinical judgement whether measures such as blood transfusions or use of antibiotics are correct in the circumstances.[11]

Everything will depend on the circumstances of the actual patient, whether the terminal stage has been reached, whether the disease is incurable and will soon prove fatal. There are clearly limits to the amount of inaction which can be practised if criminal liability is to be avoided. Inaction in a terminal stage, especially if it is in face of a new situation, such as pneumonia, is perhaps permissible, but inaction over established procedures may not be exonerated. Thus if the person was blue from heart failure of the right-sided variety, and had been much relieved by inhaling oxygen, there would be criminal liability if the doctor or nurse did not replace the oxygen cylinder when empty. Similarly a severe diabetic, who had come to rely on insulin injections, could not be ordered by the doctor to omit them in order to produce a fatal attack of diabetic coma. There are certainly limits to the degree of inaction that is legally permissible to a doctor who has undertaken the care of a patient.[12] For instance a charge could be brought against a doctor or nurse who withheld food and drink; even relatives have this obligation. Thus in Scotland a woman was found guilty of manslaughter because she failed to offer food to a bedridden woman who was her aunt.[13] On the other hand, there is no medical obligation on the doctor to offer food by unnatural channels, that is, through a gastrotomy aperture into the stomach, to someone dying in distress and unable to swallow.

The decision to suspend the use of a mechanical respirator in a patient who has suffered death of the brain, is not an example of death from inaction, or of euthanasia. Thus after a motor car accident someone may receive a severe head injury. At first it is not known whether the brain can recover, it is even impossible to know the extent of the injury. As a result of the damage to the brain, the respirations may be depressed, being very slow and shallow. Unless something were done quickly this person would die of suffocation. As a method of treatment, amounting to resuscitation, the patient is put into a mechanical respirator; this immediately corrects the defective breathing. Many people then make a full recovery; others do not and only time will tell. If damage is very severe, so that much of the brain has been destroyed, it becomes eventually clear that the brain has indeed died. There are no signs of nervous activity and even the electrical tracing (EEG) may be flat for a long period of time. The doctors in consultation then decide that the brain is dead; they decide that the patient has died; they are in a position to sign the death certificate. Once the decision is made that death has occurred, all treatment, all medicines, all feeding and nursing care cease, all machines, including the respirator, are stopped. The person has become a corpse; he is probably cold and a post-mortem examination might well reveal that parts of the body had started to putrefy. This death was not caused by turning off the respirator, by inaction. There has been much confusion on this point in the minds of the general public, although doctors are quite clear about the sequence of events.

As might be expected, there are all grades of injury to the brain, from severe injuries which cause death of this organ to those which are slight and from which full recovery occurs. As an intermediate group there are those in whom the brain is not sufficiently damaged to cause death but the patient remains unconscious for many weeks or months. Some eventually recover consciousness, they may even make a complete and lasting recovery, so that as long as there are reasonable grounds for hope, full nursing and medical care, including perhaps the use of a respirator, are offered to such a patient. As long as there are reasonable grounds of hope, the respirator must be employed, lest death from inaction occur and a criminal charge be made of manslaughter by negligence.

In modern medical care of all illnesses and injuries there are the ordinary traditional methods of medical and nursing care, which should always be employed, and the new technical achievements of respirators, heart pace-makers and circulation pumps, kidney dialysis units and so forth. Even here there is uncertainty and lack of precise definition: intravenous feeding at first was regarded as one of the new extraordinary achievements of modern medical technology, but as it became more common it began to rank as an ordinary method of treatment.

Certain moral theologians, especially those of the Roman Catholic Church, have pressed for a firm distinction between 'ordinary' methods of treatment which are mandatory and 'extraordinary' methods which remain a matter for the doctor's discretion; the latter may be omitted if this course is deemed advisable. Similarly legal experts have spoken in terms of life-preserving medical care and artificial means of keeping certain organs or functions alive in a patient in whom organs or functions essential to life have ceased to operate spontaneously.[14] These twilight areas of indecision, the nub of the euthanasia problem as regards modern medical technology, will be discussed in greater detail in chapter IV.

A doctor might be charged with murder or manslaughter if any action of his had been responsible for the death of the patient, and it has just been argued that gross examples of inaction might result in such a charge. A doctor could also be sued for negligence by the relatives of any patient who died, if they considered that the death was due to any action or inaction on the part of the doctor.

All these responsibilities of the doctor stem from the fact that he and the patient have entered into a special relationship, a covenant of mutual trust and respect. It is not merely a contract that the doctor will use all reasonable skill in the care of the patient, although this is certainly implied. Skill is defined as follows:

The physician shall have the degree of learning and skill ordinarily possessed by physicians of good standing practising in the same locality and . . . he shall use ordinary care and diligence in applying that learning and skill to the treatment of the patient. Whether he has done so in a particular case is generally a question for experts and can be established only by their testimony unless the matter at issue is within the common knowledge of laymen.[15]

Failure to achieve this exercise of skill might lead to a charge of malpractice or negligence.

The law prescribes that all reasonable skill shall be used in the care of the patient, but has seldom defined the content of the word 'care' beyond the assumption that the doctor will preserve life as long as possible with the optimal degree of healthy functioning of as many organs as possible. All his life a doctor labours to cure disease, to decrease injury, to overcome disability and to delay death. Fears of legal action and slanderous accusations, however ill-founded, provide an additional motive for treating every illness, meeting every new complication, restoring function and prolonging life. Ordinary human sympathy reinforces this drive, which is all one-way, to preserve life. Those who, somewhat light-heartedly, have advocated that a doctor should suddenly in a split second of time go into reverse and deliberately shorten life, even kill the patient, have seldom envisaged the hesitation, indecision and natural aversion of the doctor. Those who drive a motor car fast in one direction, and suddenly change into reverse, hear and feel the most shattering protest from the bowels of the gear box, and any doctor who changes gear from cure to kill feels it in the depths of his being.

What does it involve when a doctor has undertaken the care of a patient? Many would answer that a doctor undertakes two duties; to preserve life and to relieve pain. These two points were enshrined in the BMA resolution of 1969 condemning euthanasia.[16] Those who support voluntary euthanasia seldom tire of pointing to the tension, if not the contradiction, that arises in terminal illness: if a doctor prolongs life he will increase the duration of the pain, if he relieves the pain with large doses of potent drugs he may shorten life. Some consider that this stems from the Hippocratic oath, which if not binding on doctors at the present day, has nevertheless an honourable tradition in medical ethics. Thus, Fletcher, in his support for voluntary euthanasia, has written much about the 'logical contradiction at the heart of the Hippocratic oath'.

Our physicians all subscribe to that oath as the standard of their professional ethics. The contradiction is there because the oath promises two things: first to relieve suffering, and second to prolong and protect life. When the patient is in the grip of an agonizing and fatal disease, the two promises are incompatible.[17]

Those who ascribe traditions to the Hippocratic oath would do well to consult the actual wording. It says nothing specifically about relieving suffering, nothing about prolonging and preserving life. The translation of Edelstein is generally considered to be the most authoritative and the relevant section reads:

I will apply dietetic measures for the benefit of the sick according to my ability and judgment. I will keep from harm and injustice. I will neither give a deadly drug to anybody if asked for it, nor will I make a suggestion to this effect.[18]

In other words, the 'dietetic measures' or 'treatment' were planned for the benefit of the patient. Physicians in Greece had few drugs to alleviate pain, they had almost no power to influence the course of fatal disease or to prolong life. If the modern physician pays attention to the best interests of the patient, he is acting in the Hippocratic tradition.

The contradiction within the Hippocratic tradition is however present as regards voluntary euthanasia, meaning by this the deliberate termination of the life of a patient. The oath stated that the physician should do everything for the benefit of the patient but that he must not give a deadly drug in order to kill him, nor might he make any suggestion to this effect. In other words it forbad murder or assistance in a suicide. So does the law of England. According to the supporters of voluntary euthanasia the contradiction within the Hippocratic oath lies in certain conditions where the greatest benefit to be conferred on a patient would be to administer a deadly drug. That is the heart of the contradiction, or alleged contradiction, in the Hippocratic tradition.

It will only prove possible to assess the validity of this proposition, that a deadly drug and death might be the greatest benefit that could be conferred to any person sick in body and mind, after discussing in the next chapters the medical and psychological aspects of incurable, distressing disease. This will lead up to a final consideration of all the issues in the concluding chapters of the book.

Probably no one would be prepared to defend against all comers the proposition that a deadly drug should never be given to anyone and that no one should ever consent to receive it. Very exceptional circumstances may occur in war, for those about to be tortured, and for shipwrecked mariners. Very exceptional circumstances certainly arise even in times of peace; thus I call to mind an occasion when in a distant part of Africa I had to quieten a dangerous violent lunatic. I had no men to help me, no one to hold him down. I went on doubling the dose of morphine and hyoscine every two hours until I got him quiet. Then he became so quiet I thought I had killed him. He survived, but if I had killed him I should have defended my action as one of conscience and of necessity.

Without in any way accepting the proposition that it is necessary to change the law of the land to suit the alleged need to terminate the life of patients suffering from incurable distressing illness, it must be first asked whether any modification of the English law which forbids any help to the suicide would not meet the situation. Nearly forty years ago Dr Harry Roberts,[19] in one of the few medical books supporting voluntary euthanasia, stated that he would not hesitate to terminate the life of an acquiescent patient who had painful advanced incurable cancer, regardless of convention and legal formality, but he did not state categorically whether he had ever exercised this option. After saying this he went on to suggest that the best solution of this problem lay in legalizing suicide!

Suicide has ceased to be a crime in England and Wales since the Suicide Act became law in 1961. There are however penalties against aiding suicide, at least in England and Wales, but not in Scotland or Switzerland. There is no evidence in those countries that the removal of penalties has solved the questions posed by voluntary euthanasia. Even now in England, though suicide is no longer a crime, most people still regard it with horror. They feel that it is still a tragedy, especially if it occurs in a young person, healthy in body but depressed in mind.

How often does painful incurable disease provoke suicide? The matter could be studied most carefully in relation to cancer, where there are accurate statistics for the country as a whole. Thus in England and Wales about 120,000 die of cancer each year. There are some 6,000 suicides a year, but little has been published concerning the proportion of suicides who have cancer. In one series of 122 consecutive post-mortem examinations on those who had committed suicide, only three had cancer.[20] If this is any guide, and it must be emphasized that it is an inaccurate one, then out of a yearly total of 6,000 suicides possibly about 150 persons take their lives because they have cancer. If about 120,000 persons die each year of cancer, but only 150 commit suicide because they have cancer, one may hazard a guess that of those who have cancer about one in a thousand ends his life in suicide.

In slowly progressive disease such as cancer, in which a certain proportion get severe pain, one might expect that those who wish to commit suicide would make the attempt. This should be possible for almost anyone who does not leave it until he is bedridden, soon to die of the disease. The fact that so few commit suicide must suggest that few actually desire to do so, or know that they are stricken with malignant disease; or else they wait until it is too late to plan their own suicide. The fact remains however that few cancer patients ask for death. Dr Leslie Banks from his experience of the cancer wards in the Middlesex Hospital, London, stated that 'the patients, however ill they were and however much they suffered, never asked for death'.[21] Perhaps they were afraid to ask, but in their own homes all the commonest methods of poisoning are close to hand and most can secure them, barbiturate, aspirin and other sedative tablets. Some would have access to a gas oven.

For an attempt at suicide to succeed, it is essential that no one should rush the poisoned person off to hospital. Regional Poisoning Treatment centres have been set up in most areas of Britain to cope with the large number of patients who have attempted to commit suicide from whatever cause. After admission to one of these units only 1·5% die, so effective are the modern methods of resuscitation. Those who die from suicide do so at home, because of the very large dose taken, but the most important factor lies in the interval of time between taking the poison and starting resuscitation at the poison centre. If someone who had cancer wished to commit suicide it would be important that some friend or relative should agree to delay calling in medical help. Possibly more cancer patients than we realize actually commit suicide, but relatives and even doctors draw a veil over the suspicious circumstances. They might attribute death to cancer alone, and this the more readily if the person was near to death. Doctors must not feel that this allows them to escape from the whole issue of voluntary euthanasia, for they alone can say what disease is present, whether it is curable, whether it will be painful, and when it may cause death. Without these four facts a person may attempt suicide, even take his own life, under a misapprehension. It should be remembered that for every single successful suicide there are eight unsuccessful attempts, possibly by people who were wishing someone to hear their cry for help.

Suicide to terminate life in a painful, distressing illness has at least one advantage over all other methods of voluntary euthanasia: it demonstrates that the person chose death; but by itself it tells us nothing about whether this was an impetuous wilful act or a settled determined wish to end life. It is generally conceded by those who support voluntary euthanasia that for many people suicide does not provide the answer. It is therefore contended that legislation is necessary. Questions at once emerge. What categories of people can choose euthanasia and what are the safeguards against abuse? It will not prove possible to answer the question of safeguards until the medical and psychological aspects of voluntary euthanasia have been considered in the ensuing two chapters. Attention will be directed first to the categories of persons for whom legislation on voluntary euthanasia is contemplated. This is the more important because it has always been envisaged that the doctors would not only advise the applicants for euthanasia but that they would administer the fatal dose.

The proposed categories of persons who might ask to receive euthanasia differ considerably from time to time and reflect the varied aims of the protagonists. The original proposals of Dr Killick Millard[22] enshrined in the Voluntary Euthanasia Bill (1936) envisaged only persons having fatal painful disease, who had informed their relatives and had put their affairs in order. Euthanasia would be restricted to those having one of the diseases on a Schedule approved by the Minister of Health of all those diseases which were 'incurable, fatal and painful'. It was not envisaged that voluntary euthanasia could be extended to include elderly demented persons (senile dementia) or children, neither of whom could swear an application before the magistrate. After this the application was to be sent to the special Referee for consideration in one of the appointed Courts.

Professor Glanville Williams in his comprehensive study of euthanasia in 1958 analysed the reasons for the rejection of the Voluntary Euthanasia Bill of 1936, which arose out of Millard's suggestions, and judged that the suggested safeguards had been too onerous. Glanville Williams was however convinced that a certain number of doctors were deliberately terminating the lives of some of their patients who had a fatal, incurable painful illness. Strictly speaking this was illegal and it was this illegality, he considered, which restrained the hands of many medical practitioners. His proposed Bill

would provide that no medical practitioner should be guilty of an offence in respect of an act done intentionally to accelerate the death of a patient who is seriously ill, unless it is proved that the act was not done in good faith with the consent of the patient and for the purpose of saving him from severe pain in an illness believed to be of an incurable and fatal character.[23]

The initiative remained, apparently with the doctor; he might approach any patient who had a painful, incurable, fatal complaint. No patient would have a right to euthanasia.[24] In other words no one had a legal right to choose death; only when death was an inevitable conclusion to an illness could a doctor approach the patient for consent. Glanville Williams did not apparently envisage euthanasia of elderly demented persons, a procedure to which he has remained totally opposed.[25]

The basis of selection of candidates for voluntary euthanasia shifted radically in Lord Raglan's Bill in 1969. It was no longer the doctor who selected but the patient who demanded, and demanded as of right. This was because there had been a shift of opinion among the supporters of voluntary euthanasia in the ten years preceding the 1969 Bill. Indicative of this trend, and accentuating this tendency, were the powerful pleas contained in the book *Voluntary Euthanasia and the Right to Death*, published in 1969. Voluntary euthanasia was no longer to be restricted to those having incurable, painful, fatal disease, at a stage when the doctor felt that it was appropriate, it was to be demanded as a right in any incurable distressing complaint.

Thus those who were permanently paralysed, or incurably disabled, or incapacitated by arthritis, or distressed by disfiguring incurable skin disorders, could all, as of right, ask for euthanasia.

In the Voluntary Euthanasia Bill (1969) a second principle of selection governed other categories of disease, for it was designed to cover persons who had reduced mental powers and could not legally exercise their choice to die. They might have an incurable mental disorder which destroyed their personality. In particular, many fear very deeply the humiliation of senile dementia. An advance declaration could be signed by young adults and, if confirmed a year later, would remain in force, unless revoked, for life. The advance declaration asked for euthanasia at the discretion of the doctor if the person became incapable of a rational existence and so incapable of giving directions. The advance declaration was probably designed largely to cope with the problem of senile dementia, but if signed and re-executed within twelve months by an adult person it would have requested euthanasia in *all* forms of incurable mental disorders, such as incurable schizophrenia and incurable forms of mania and depression. No one in the debate in the House of Lords on the 1969 Bill commented on these categories of persons. As the Bill had as a basic principle the right of a mature person to choose death, it excluded persons below 18 years as minors, and adults who had lost their mental faculties, unless they had signed an advance declaration while in full possession of their mental powers.

Those who oppose voluntary euthanasia are often accused of employing the 'thin edge of the wedge' argument, and of asserting that terminating the life of the dying cancer patient is but the 'thin edge of the wedge'. The 'wedge' argument was brilliantly pilloried by Glanville Williams in 1958,[26] and eleven years later he reiterated his arguments that 'the ancient wedge argument . . . is the trump card of the traditionalist because no proposal for reform, however strong the arguments, is immune from the wedge objection.'[27]

Even if he accepts these strictures, it is nevertheless not unreasonable for the student of proposals to legalize voluntary euthanasia to ask what principles are involved in the selection of persons to be allowed to choose euthanasia and what categories emerge in practice. Let us return to the line taken by Glanville Williams because it represents the development of a carefully considered plan. He started from the principle that 'euthanasia, the merciful extinction of life where it is performed upon a dying person with his consent and is the only way of relieving his sufferings'[28] is justifiable. These words occur in the opening sentence of his chapter on euthanasia. Having enlisted our sympathy, if not our support, he proceeded to make a 'legislative suggestion'[29] for voluntary euthanasia. The basis of this suggeston was to do 'no more than give legislative blessing to the practice that the great weight of medical opinion approves'.[30] The complete list of categories of persons to whom doctors might with the consent of the patient administer euthanasia then went on to include:

1. A dying person, if it is the only way to relieve his suffering.[31]
2. Earlier stages of incurable fatal disease, that would eventually cause severe pain.[32]
3. Minors, that is children and adolescents, at the discretion of the doctor who would take 'into account, as he always does, the wishes of the parents as well as those of the child'.[33]

(Speaking, I may say, as someone who was a paediatrician for many years, I find myself boggling at the idea of ascertaining the wishes of an adolescent girl who has developed cancer about her own euthanasia.) But Glanville Williams goes on to yet 'other proposals for euthanasia', suggesting the following categories:

4. 'Incapacitating but non-painful afflictions such as paralysis.'[34]
5. 'Hopelessly [mentally] defective children', subject to the parents' wishes; likewise [physically] handicapped children.[35]
6. Prisoners and the criminally insane, who might prefer suicide or euthanasia to long-term imprisonment.[36]

Whether all this illustrates how the 'thin end of the wedge' actually operates must be left to the judgment of the reader.

Adamantly adhering to the principle of free and informed consent, except in minors where the parents exercise their rights of choice, Glanville Williams could not favour the euthanasia of elderly demented persons (senile dementia).[37]

Lord Raglan's Voluntary Euthanasia Bill (1969) had as its basic principle the right to die, and, as an implementing clause, the signing of an advance declaration to cover the loss of mental faculties if senile dementia eventually occurred in old age. It included all 'serious disease or impairment reasonably thought in my case to be incurable and to cause me severe distress or render me incapable of rational existence'. It was therefore not restricted to fatal disease; any incurable distressing complaint would qualify. It was not restricted to people who were dying of their complaint; it could be chosen by the patient, as of right, even in the earliest stage of the disorder, provided that the consultant and the other doctor stated that it was incurable and would eventually cause severe distress. The advance declaration, designed probably to cover the onset of senile dementia, would, for those who had signed it, have made euthanasia mandatory in all incurable mental disorders. It must be asked whether the majority of long-stay patients in a mental hospital are not suffering from such disorders. When the author debated voluntary euthanasia at the London Hospital in 1971 with a consultant psychiatrist from the Maudsley Hospital, a supporter of voluntary euthanasia, he acknowledged this to be the case.

Again, whether this illustrates how the 'thin end of the wedge' actually operates must be left to the judgment of the reader.

Anyone who has followed the 'wedge' argument will realize that it is quite impossible to answer a simple question such as 'Do you approve of voluntary euthanasia?' Yet some 2,000 doctors in 1964 and 1965 were asked in an opinion poll, 'If voluntary euthanasia became permissible, would you be prepared to administer it?'[38] It is probable that they all envisaged only one category, namely that mentioned above, 'the terminal stages of a distressing and incurable illness', because these very words were used in the first lines of the questionnaire. It is unlikely that they envisaged the five other categories regarded with some favour by Glanville Williams, still less the categories of incurable mental disorders that would be included for those who had signed an advance declaration under Lord Raglan's Voluntary Euthanasia Bill (1969).

All the foregoing, the writings of Professor Glanville Williams and Lord Raglan's Voluntary Euthanasia Bill (1969) envisaged only *voluntary* euthanasia. The patient must have a determined rational desire for death, the patient must consent. It remained for an American moral theologian, Joseph Fletcher, to point out the limitations of voluntary euthanasia.

What of the patient who has never stated his wishes and is past making a mentally competent choice [for enthanasia]? Under this code [of voluntary euthanasia] mercy would have to be denied no matter how hideous and hopeless his sufferings. Yet in modern medical practice most [dying] patients are in precisely this submoral condition.[39]

It is evident from his writings that Professor Fletcher has spent much of his time visiting patients in hospital, for he also says:

The classical deathbed scene with its loving partings and solemn last words is practically a thing of the past. In its stead is a sedated, comatose, betubed object, manipulated and subconscious, if not subhuman.[40]

If modern medical technology can prolong life, is not death increasingly determined by medical decisions to terminate life in someone dying? Fuddled and muddled, too often the patient is past knowing what decisions are being taken for his benefit. This must not be dismissed by the caption 'involuntary euthanasia'. It can only be hoped that all the decisions are humanely undergirded by the Hippocratic tradition that everything must be done for the benefit of the patient. The relatives might add: not only be done, but be seen to be done, with regard for the feelings not only of the patient but also of those who stand and wait.

IV

Medical Aspects

Preliminary

Those who favour legislation on voluntary euthanasia adduce various medical reasons in support of their claim. They state that people who have incurable fatal disease should be offered the choice of euthanasia. In this chapter we will investigate how the doctor arrives at the diagnosis of an incurable fatal disease, and in the subsequent chapter how the patient receives this news and how he reacts towards it; that is to say, the psychological aspects of mortal illness.

Various charges are brought against the medical profession by those who support legislation on voluntary euthanasia. Some maintain that doctors prolong life when this is undesirable; others believe that there are far too many elderly people in our modern society. It will be necessary to examine these propositions.

The most recent English book advocating voluntary euthanasia contained articles by twelve contributors, only three of whom were doctors, none of whom was either a general medical practitioner or a geriatrician or a consultant physician or surgeon. One article by a doctor, the editor of a medical journal, gave a masterly review of the history of suicide and voluntary euthanasia.[1] Another article by a pathologist could not discuss from personal experience the problems that arise in terminal illness.[2] One would have valued, however, the experience peculiar to pathologists, for they ascertain at the post-mortem examination the real causes of death. How far do these agree with the opinions of the clinician about the diseases considered to be present during life? Any decision for euthanasia would be made by a clinician and it is to be hoped that there would often be some check at a subsequent autopsy. The third medical article in the book was by a distinguished consultant psychiatrist. Since at the present time depressive illness, usually curable by modern treatment, often results in suicide, one would have valued some discussion concerning whether depression might lead to an application for euthanasia. Again, since senile dementia is one of the mental illnesses that would have qualified for euthanasia, under the provisions of the advance declaration, one would have valued some discussion on the criteria by which a psychiatrist would distinguish the pathological condition of senile dementia from the physiological condition of an ageing brain found in all elderly persons. The considered opinion of this consultant psychiatrist is most disturbing: 'no clear line can be drawn between physiological and pathological processes in this connection.'[3] But, in practice would not the psychiatrist have to divide persons into one or other category in order to determine if euthanasia could be administered to an elderly demented person under the terms of the advance declaration of the Voluntary Euthanasia Bill (1969)? There was no discussion of the assessment of reduced mental faculties that would lead a consultant psychiatrist to consider recommending euthanasia. Speaking as a doctor, I would like to know these specifications before signing the blank cheque of the advance declaration.

It appears that no detailed medical article or book has been written in recent years to support legislation on voluntary euthanasia. No general medical practitioner, no physician, surgeon or geriatrician has written telling us how many patients have asked for euthanasia. They have not stated whether they indeed did occasionally terminate the life of someone who was dying. They have not stated whether they did terminate the life of someone who had still a fair period of rational, conscious personal life before him, albeit racked with pain and distress that defied all therapy. It is understandable that doctors still in practice would be loath to give details, but some in retirement might be moved to state their case. They say they have a case for legislation on euthanasia. It is very difficult to answer a case that is never put forward in any detail, supported by concrete facts and figures, but one that is supported only by numerous anecdotes.

'Too many people live too long'

Those who support legislation on voluntary euthanasia often refer to the fact that there are too many elderly people. In addition it is stated

that the total population is rising. There is also considerable apprehension that individual lives are being prolonged too long, even when
the quality of personal life is negligible.

These facts are set forth as if the tendency towards old age will
increase indefinitely and the problem will get worse. 'In ten years
time there will be nine million in this country over 65, i.e. one sixth
of the total population, and the proportion is likely to increase' wrote
one of the medical supporters of voluntary euthanasia. His readers
were therefore enjoined to accept the biblical allowance of three-
score years and ten and

to opt out for death at, say, 75, rather than peter out in increasing dependence on others . . . A recent TV programme painted a pathetic picture of
aged persons living in misery and loneliness, burdens both to themselves
and those whose devotion and sense of duty impelled them to sacrificial
service on their behalf.[4]

These are certainly real fears and must be examined in detail.

Let us consider first the general question of overpopulation. It is
true that world population is doubling every thirty years, increasing
on an average about 1·8% a year. This rapid rate of growth however
is no longer true of Britain. A decade ago our population was increasing about 0·8% a year, but since 1964 there has been a steady drop in
the birth rate. A slight but probably temporary rise occurred in 1970
following the birth pill scare. Nowadays the increase is only 0·3% a
year. Estimates of population in the later decades of the present century have therefore been scaled down. There is no knowledge whether
the birth rate will continue to fall and speculation would be unwise.
As far as can be seen at the present time there are no longer grounds
for fearing a serious threat of overpopulation in Britain; this is a new
fact, confirmed by all academic centres of population study, but not
generally realized.

It is true that in the last few centuries many people in advanced
countries have been living to a greater age. The vital statistics of
Switzerland in the seventeenth century are regarded as some of the
most accurate in Europe. At that time, some three hundred years ago,
a baby born in Switzerland had an expectation of life for some 33
years; at the present time it is at least 66 years. This means that the
proportion of retired persons in the total population has increased
enormously especially during the present century. In 1920 slightly
over 5% of the population of England and Wales were over 65 years
of age, but in 1970 the proportion had risen to about 12·5%. At

present there are in England and Wales some two million people aged 75 years and over; they should perhaps be encouraged, according to one of the doctors who supports voluntary euthanasia,

to opt out of life when they want to – in full possession of their faculties, with their families gathered round them. Such an end could be a joyful and triumphant occasion. Away with all this hypocrisy of funerals and misery.[5]

While it is true that the expectation of life has increased dramatically in recent years, it is not generally realized that we seem probably to be over the crest of the wave in England and Wales and in certain other advanced countries. A recent World Health Organization Report pointed out that in the period 1955–60 there was a slight but unexpected rise in the mortality rates of the entire population in eight advanced countries. In the period 1960–69 the tendency became more widespread and there was a slight increase in the mortality rates in sixteen advanced countries of Europe and America, including Britain and the United States.[6] It would be unwise to speculate about the causes here save to note that opinion inclines to a view that some of the killing degenerative diseases, such as coronary thrombosis, are more frequent under conditions of mental stress and muscular inactivity, such as occur in motor-car driving. Stress operates in other ways, and other injurious factors such as cigarette-smoking, high blood pressure, even luxury diets and obesity all play a part. Pollution too may be a factor in the increased mortality. Whatever are the causes of this slight increase in the mortality rates it also means that modern medical technology is still relatively ineffective in prolonging life. Resuscitation techniques, methods of intensive care, artificial intravenous feeding, cardiac pacemakers and antibiotics impress the onlooker very much, especially if he is not medically qualified. Doubtless in some individuals they do prolong lives; it seems as if General Eisenhower was just not allowed to die of coronary heart disease. Taken as a whole these methods have not proved very successful in elderly persons. Thus antibiotics do not control infections so well in persons of advanced age; the mortality rate even in treated cases rises throughout adult life. Indeed mortality rates from most infections which are low in early adolescence, rise by about 5% of this figure for every year of adult life. It has been pointed out that, if mortality could be maintained at the optimal low figure reached at the age of ten, man would have a life expectancy of eight hundred years.[7] Pneumonia is still in very truth the old man's friend, even although antibiotics are given.

A baby born in England at the present time ought to live to rather more than 65 years, but for someone who has reached 65 years of age the further expectation of life has risen by rather less than one additional year (when compared with those of a similar age) since the beginning of the century.[8] Professor Hinton has stated the problem in terms of those who are still in the prime of life.

Once the age (of fifty years) has been reached modern conditions have not been so successful in further prolonging life expectancy. The fifty-year old man of 1911 could expect about another twenty years of life. Half a century later this had only been increased to about twenty-two years. It is a meagre advance, which reflects our comparative failure to make much headway in the prevention or cure of the serious diseases and deteriorations of middle and old age.[9]

In the United States 'the mean life span has remained essentially constant at around 70 years since the 1950s.'[10] Great store may be set on the conquest of cancer, but if it was eliminated completely mean life-expectancy would be increased by only about 2·5 years; if cardio-vascular disease (mainly atherosclerosis as shewn in coronary heart disease and cerebral strokes) were eliminated then some ten years more life could be anticipated. Even if the two commonest causes of death were completely overcome, the mean life expectation would only be prolonged to a little over 80 years of age. In the end old age catches up on us. There is at present total inability to control the process of ageing.

The proportion of old people in the population of Britain has reached a high but almost stationary level, a fact known to the experts, even if it has hardly become general knowledge. Sir Herbert Telley, the Government Actuary said, as early as 1966, that the belief that Britain faced the problem of an ageing population because the expectation of life was increasing and there were more old people to support was a fallacy. Projections prepared in his department showed that the average age was in fact steadily falling.[11]

It is indeed amazing to find how many persons consider that Providence has decreed for man a natural span of life of three score years and ten, and that the Bible teaches this, but people seldom read the whole verse even in the Psalm, and never in a modern translation.

> Seventy years is the span of our life,
> eighty if our strength holds;
> the hurrying years are labour and sorrow,
> so quickly they pass and are forgotten.[12]

The idea that three score years and ten are part of the divine plan does not die easily; it has almost a medicated survival in the modern literature of euthanasia.

Resuscitation of the elderly

This must not be taken to deny that there are many grim stories of the medicated survival of elderly persons and of efforts at resuscitation, both of which may prove very harrowing. Most of these methods are new and it is right that their use and abuse should be debated within the medical profession assisted by legitimate criticism from the general public. Thus a geriatric nurse wrote to the *Guardian*[13] about an old woman aged over 100 being given a blood transfusion. Perhaps the relevant questions were whether it made her more comfortable or merely prolonged her life, and actually what were her own wishes on the matter. These points are seldom mentioned in such protests. There are however many genuine informed complaints.

A retired consultant physician wrote with concern in 1971,

Since I retired I have seen with alarm the treatment of some aged relations and friends – for example: A confused but happy lady, aged 90, cared for by her daughter in a nursing home, having fallen out of bed, was sent to hospital to be 'pinned'. Acute dyspnoea after operation was not treated, apparently from fear she might succumb from effects of drugs. When she died on the fourth day the house surgeon applied external cardiac massage. The daughter, a State-registered nurse, who was present, asked that she should be left in peace. The reply was, 'I have my duty to do' . . . I look forward to my own old age as ever with distaste, but now with dread.[14]

It is good that these misgivings should be ventilated, especially when they apply to elderly people. A Birmingham consultant physician wrote recently:

'When my turn comes,' I said [to a medical ward sister], 'I want to die in peace, and I've written "Not to be resuscitated" in my diary.' 'That's no good,' she replied, 'I've got "Not for . . ."' (and she mentioned the telephone number that summons the cardiac arrest team) tattooed across here,' pointing to the top of her chest. I would have liked to ask to see it, but my courage failed.[15]

He is not alone in this attitude. Lord Platt, a former President of the Royal College of Physicians has stated publicly that at his age (over 70) he would refuse cardiac resuscitation.[16] If he collapsed or became unconscious, how would he make his wishes known? (On this point see Appendix D below).

Decisions concerning whether to resuscitate elderly people are difficult. The fact that some successes followed resuscitation in young patients led doctors at first to try these methods on everyone, whatever their age. Some doctors then began to criticize openly the use of these methods on the elderly, especially those who were dying. Cases of heroic resuscitation, unnecessary investigation and meddlesome treatment were reported in the medical journals. A tragic instance of a doctor who was 'not allowed to die' has already been quoted at length,[17] and has also been reported extensively in the literature in support of legislation for voluntary euthanasia.[18] However, all attempts to restrict the resuscitation of the elderly have met with serious difficulties, and are apt to cause emotional reactions and misunderstandings if they are publicized. Thus in 1967 the following notice appeared on the appropriate boards of Neasden Hospital in London:

The following patients are not to be resuscitated: very elderly, over 65; malignant disease. Chronic chest disease. Chronic renal disease.
Top of yellow treatment card to be marked NTBR [i.e. Not To Be Resuscitated].
The following people should be resuscitated: collapse as the result of diagnostic and therapeutic procedures – e.g. needle in pleura (even if over 65 years). Sudden unexpected collapse under 65 years – i.e. loss of consciousness, cessation of breathing, no carotid pulsation.

Dr W. F. T. McMath, the medical superintendent, had addressed this notice to all physicians and ward sisters and only after careful consultation was it published; but he was criticized by a board of enquiry appointed by the Minister of Health for the blunt wording and for publicly displaying the notice. It was also suggested by the board that nobody should be excluded from resuscitation only because of age. Possibly the notice would have hung on the notice boards for several more months if it had not been discovered accidentally by a BBC television team. The matter came in for a good deal of newspaper publicity, but several doctors publicly stated their support for Dr McMath.[19]

Similar difficulties were encountered in 1969 when the Medical Officer of Health of Eastbourne tried to formulate resuscitation policy in the geriatric hospitals of that town. He advised that patients over 80 years of age should not be resuscitated after a heart attack. There was no intention to deny resuscitation to those who were mentally alert or physically fit. At once there was a popular outcry in the national press, and ill-considered reports suggested that patients over 80 years were being put down. The doctor defended his point of view at some length in a medical newspaper. He considered that an elderly person should be allowed to die a natural death and he had received several hundreds of letters supporting this point of view. It was of interest that most of the letters received did not concern malignant disease, the final stages of which last usually only a few months. Most letters concerned those who had lived for several years after a stroke, or were paralysed from a nervous complaint, or housebound from severe arthritis. Few letters came from the sufferers themselves or quoted what they themselves said; they came from the relatives, who were feeling much strain. It is far more easy to assess their misery than that of the sufferer, who often remains strangely silent about his real desires.

All this indicates a problem of enormous dimensions containing much human misery both for the patient and for the relatives. It calls for much study and requires public debate. There are those who feel it requires legislation on voluntary euthanasia, but the Medical Officer of Health of Eastbourne was emphatic that 'for society [legislation] would create more problems than it would solve'.[20] He castigated those who said that, if an elderly patient was denied the latest wonder drug in terminal illness, this was 'modified euthanasia'; in other words that doctors were already administering euthanasia. The debate concerning euthanasia has certainly been clouded by many hazy definitions.

A novel method of checking the unnecessary resuscitation of elderly persons was put forward recently by Sir George Thomson, Vice-President of the Voluntary Euthanasia Society.[21] He did not advocate any change in the laws enacted by Parliament but asked doctors to consider a fundamental change in medical ethics so that the useless prolongation of life should become an offence for any member of the medical profession. Presumably doctors who committed this offence would be disciplined by the General Medical Council, in the same way as doctors who disregard the recognized ethical code of their profession. (Any doctor who advertises his services, or who has sexual relationships with one of his patients, can, after examination before the General Medical Council, be disciplined, and in serious cases struck off the Medical Register.) Sir George considered that doctors might be disciplined for the crime of prolonging a useless life. The law of the land is that doctors may be sued for

malpractice in the ordinary civil courts if they have not used reasonable professional skill. If they are found negligent, damages may be
awarded. The proposal to discipline doctors before the General
Medical Council for prolonging a life which was of little value can be
described as incredibly naive. Anyone reading further this chapter
will have some insight into the complexity of the problem. It does
still exist, however – that of prolonging a life of low quality, while the
law of the land regards any deliberate substantial shortening of life as
murder. There is certainly an unresolved tension here.

For a balanced discussion of the numerous facets of this problem
in elderly persons the reader is referred to any modern text-book on
geriatrics. Dr John Agate devotes a whole chapter to this problem.[22]
It is impossible to compress twenty pages into a few lines.

The use of 'crash call' emergency measures to resuscitate a very elderly
patient after cardiac arrest must be questionable . . . [It] is not primarily a
question of age; least of all is it right for us to select an arbitrary age barrier
and forbid resuscitation for people beyond it. Many factors have to be
taken into account, and a cheerful, active and well-integrated patient with
a good prognosis otherwise might be a good recipient for extreme measures
like these. However, when a heart stops or pulmonary embolus happens in
a very elderly ill patient, the staffs of geriatric wards will usually think it
merciful and will not try to resuscitate. Is this then at variance with the
observation that many patients in geriatric wards are found to be having
transfusions or infusions of fluid, and some are having naso-gastric tube
feeding? This is often because blood transfusion is curative, confers long-
term benefits, or gives short-term relief from symptoms, while intravenous
(into a vein) or intra-gastric (into the stomach) therapy is being used to
combat dehydration. [Dehydration – loss of fluids – can cause very painful
thirst, which may prove fatal.] . . . Most doctors shrink from letting any
patient die a horrible death from starvation or dehydration. This is the
usual explanation, then, of tube-feeding in long-stay wards of irremediable
patients: and who shall say it is cruel?

This however may not be understood by the general public; it may
even not be understood by a nurse who works in a geriatric ward.
Mention has already been made of a letter from one such nurse which
appeared in *The Guardian* in 1967, asserting

the stark truth that all patients dying of old age must now expect, as a
matter of routine, to be forced through an additional period, sometimes a
long period, of pain and/or acute discomfort, before death finally comes.

She gave two examples out of many in her experience: a dying woman
over 100 who was given a blood transfusion, and, secondly, a senile
man, who had gangrene, who was kept alive with artificial feeding

and a urinary apparatus.[23] (According to Agate, however, a blood transfusion can give relief from symptoms even if it is not curative, while artificial feeding may be necessary to prevent thirst; and the removal of the urinary apparatus would certainly result in a blockage of micturition, which might cause one of the most severe pains which can afflict any man.) If, however, these measures appeared cruel to a geriatric nurse, how much more difficult would it be to explain them all to those with little medical knowledge? This is not to say that there are no errors of clinical judgment or of nursing skill in geriatric wards, for these occur in all sections of medical work. Patients and relatives may complain to the staff or to the hospital board. If negligence is flagrant, a remedy can be sought in the civil courts, either against hospital boards or against doctors. No reference has however been traced to a case of alleged negligence in prolonging life of low quality. Until such a case is brought in the civil courts it would appear to be presumptuous to say what legal arguments would be brought forward, what compromise struck between the traditional duty of a doctor to preserve life and the more recently defined duty to overcome pain.

Incurable diseases

Many of those who advocate legislation for voluntary euthanasia wish to confine it to incurable diseases. The Voluntary Euthanasia Bill (1969) spoke of an 'irremediable condition', meaning 'a serious physical illness or impairment reasonably thought in the patient's case to be incurable and expected to cause him severe distress or render him incapable of rational existence'. Two physicians, one being of consultant status, were to certify that the patient appeared to be suffering from an 'irremediable condition'. Two categories of incurable disease were envisaged in the Bill. There were firstly 'serious physical diseases' of the body. There were, secondly, those conditions of the mind in which the person was 'incapable of rational existence'. Both the physical diseases and the psychiatric disorders had to be 'reasonably thought in the patient's case to be incurable'. It must be clearly recognized that the Voluntary Euthanasia Bill (1969) did not specify that the disease (physical or psychiatric) should be a fatal disorder; it did specify that it should be one 'expected to cause . . . severe distress'.

The first Euthanasia Bill (1936) had restricted voluntary euthanasia to those 'suffering from an incurable, fatal and painful disease'. Indeed the Minister of Health had been asked in this Bill to form a Schedule of these 'incurable, fatal, painful diseases' because euthanasia could only be administered if two medical practitioners certified the presence of one of the scheduled diseases. The Bill had been proposed by Dr Killick Millard, a Medical Officer of Health. He had been accustomed to receive notification of infectious diseases listed on the official schedule and it seemed to him, that it should be possible to compile another schedule of 'incurable, fatal, painful diseases'. This would have provided an administrative difficulty of the greatest magnitude. Increased knowledge of the essential variability of disease has made it impossible to compile this list, although those who are not medically qualified still believe that certain diseases are inherently incurable, and some are inevitably fatal. A few examples will be considered in order to expose this fallacy.

It is extremely difficult to know what diseases, even under the later Voluntary Euthanasia Bill (1969) might have been deemed to be, on occasions, a 'serious physical illness, incurable, and likely to cause distress'. Almost all forms of cancer and leukaemia spring to mind, together with serious forms of coronary heart disease, many forms of paralysis, including that following a stroke; also chronic bronchitis, chronic disease of the liver (cirrhosis) and kidney (chronic nephritis), and certain chronic diseases of the bone (Paget's disease) and skin (certain varieties of dermatitis). Is osteo-arthritis not incurable? Should the blindness of old age, or senile deafness not qualify? Where does the list end? The majority of the chronic degenerative diseases of middle age would qualify; although alleviated, even improved, they cannot be cured; they may cause much distress; so they are serious. With regard to the psychiatric diseases which are incurable and deprive a person of his rational powers, it could be stated that most of the long-term patients in a psychiatric hospital would appear to qualify for euthanasia if they had signed an advance declaration.

Cancer

Let us consider the question of cancer; it is the disorder *par excellence* for which voluntary euthanasia appears designed. Cancer is really not one disease, but a large group of diseases having certain characteristics, in that they tend, unless successfully treated, to spread to other parts of the body. Many different varieties occur. One cancer, called a rodent ulcer of the skin, can be successfully removed by a minor operation and hardly ever recurs. The rate of cure is over 99 %. Other forms of cancer are not so curable, but certain other varieties, if seen early by the surgeon, have quite an appreciable percentage of 'clinical cures', patients who survive five, ten, fifteen or more years, with no sign of a recurrence.

Unfortunately a certain proportion of patients, even after the best treatment, develop recurrences, even in distant parts of the body. Some of these recurrences can be treated by surgical operations or other forms of treatment. Complete cure may then occur, or many months or years of health may result before any further recurrences appear. Unfortunately recurrences are often widespread and cannot be treated effectively.

In the majority of patients the diagnosis of a recurrence of cancer can be reasonably certain. Thereafter does death always follow? Undoubtedly on rare occasions complete cure, called a remission, of proved and widespread recurrences of cancer at many different sites can occur. There is an extensive literature on the subject, rare as the event is. Thus in American medical journals over 1,000 cases have been reported by a wide variety of doctors in whom widespread recurrences (metastases) of cancer occurred, and although the patient was given no treatment at all, all the masses disappeared.[24] These cases of the apparent cure of widespread, inoperable cancer were reported because the doctor had in almost every case confirmed the recurrence, having had a piece of tissue removed for microscopical examination.

In Britain recognition of this fact, although rare, has encouraged the formation of a special Cancer Registry in 1960.[25] Thus one patient was found to have cancer at an abdominal operation so widespread that the numerous masses had not been removed, but these disappeared without treatment, and no trace of cancer was found even at a post-mortem examination conducted some sixteen years later.[26] Conferences have been convened even recently at which several papers were given on this subject,[27] for it demonstrates that the body has defence mechanisms of an immunological character against certain forms of cancer. If these forces were better understood they could be modified and employed to cure cancer regarded at present as hopeless. A regression of untreated cancer is commoner in certain varieties, being most frequent in chorion-epithelioma (a rare disease occurring in women after pregnancy); it is commoner in children, being assessed by various observers at rates which vary from 1 to 8 %.[28]

In order to place these startling facts in their true perspective, it must be emphasized that, in the large majority of patients suffering from the later stages of widespread inoperable cancer, the disease usually progresses relentlessly forward. Sometimes the march of the disease may be rapid, especially if vital structures happen to be involved, or serious infection supervenes, but in other patients it may be very slow. Thus among a series of 250 completely *untreated* patients, suffering from confirmed cancer of the breast, a group of doctors at the Middlesex Hospital, London,[29] reported cases who survived for as long as eighteen years, many of whom had little pain. They reported that 'all published series on this subject contain instances of prolonged survival' of untreated persons.

The early stages of almost all varieties of cancer can be treated by surgery, radio-therapy and other forms of treatment. Treated thus, a fair proportion of people live a healthy life, with no sign of recurrence for many years, even for the remainder of their lives. As matters stand at present in Britain, probably most of these people never realize that they have had cancer. Why should they? Most doctors have had experiences such as the following true story of mine. About sixteen years ago, just before I left Africa, a young doctor came to me in great distress. His young wife had had a small and apparently harmless pimple removed from her skin and he had heard that the report had just been received that it was a most malignant variety of skin cancer. He asked what should be done. After a long talk we concluded that it was best to wait until something further occurred. Nothing has done, except the birth of three children. She is still alive and very well. It is probable now that there will never be any recurrence. A host of similar cases have been reported.[30] Late recurrences after thirty-five years[31] and even fifty years have been reported.[32] Others never get a recurrence. There is much to be said for shielding the patient from the full dread truth at the early curable stage of the disease, but an intelligent minority press persistently for the full truth and are entitled to it. Even more are entitled to the truth, especially if they demand it, when obvious suspicious recurrences occur.

In many people a long interval of time elapses between the treatment of the original malignant disease and its recurrence. Often other less serious diseases, have intervened, perhaps causing pain in the back from a slipped disc or chest pain from pneumonia. When the recurrences appear, perhaps in distant parts of the body, it may be a long time before the diagnosis can be established with any degree of certainty. Perhaps it is thought that the chest pain is only due to another attack of pneumonia, or the back pain to the slipped disc. Suspicions may be aroused at an X-ray examination, but conclusive proof may be lacking unless some piece of tissue can be removed and examined microscopically. A consultant surgeon with much experience of the disease may be reasonably certain, especially if he sees the person on more than one occasion and can detect progressive changes which are fairly characteristic of a recurrence of malignant disease. Evidence slowly piles up, but it is extremely difficult to know the precise day when the diagnosis becomes reasonably certain. Experience has taught the surgeon the uncertainties that attend the diagnosis. All this has a profound bearing on the question: Should a doctor tell? This question must be reworded: 'When is a surgeon sufficiently certain to be able to tell?' It has a profound bearing on the question when, if ever, a patient suffering from a recurrence of cancer, might apply for voluntary euthanasia. (The psychological shock, involving denial of the facts or depression, which the patient may experience on hearing that cancer is present is discussed in the next chapter.)

Many of the recurrences of cancer are painless, and most of those who have cancer die peacefully in their sleep. Surveys of hospital patients reveal that about a quarter of the cancer patients are liable to pain.[33] This pain is usually well controlled in hospital. Certain special institutions make a point of admitting cancer patients who have been getting much pain: they report that it is always possible to control pain. They quote success in about 97 to 99% of cases, and ascribe the failures to psychological factors.[34] Injections may be required at frequent intervals by day and by night and it is not always possible to provide these facilities for those dying at home.

Recurrences in certain positions may cause much pain, but it is possible to relieve this pain with regular injections. Dr Cicely Saunders observed a large series of some 220 hospital patients in their last illness; 33 had cancer, over half of whom had no pain; one quarter required narcotic drugs (morphine, pethidine or levorphanol) for an average duration of six and a half weeks.[35] She commented that some patients with osteo-arthritis and rheumatoid arthritis had more severe pain, often for many years, than the cancer patients, but could not be relieved with narcotic drugs, because of the risk of addiction. It is therefore relevant to ask whether voluntary euthanasia should not be offered to chronic arthritics, even although their illness is not fatal.

Hodgkin's disease, leukaemia

Every year now fresh advances are made in the treatment of cancer and allied conditions such as lymphadenoma (Hodgkin's disease) and leukaemia. Until recently Hodgkin's disease would have been regarded as almost invariably fatal; now over 40% of early cases, if adequately treated by radio-therapy, appear free of disease at the end of ten years. Certain forms of leukaemia with modern treatment survive in health for several years although formerly death occurred in a comparatively short space of time. Even before modern treatment was evolved, a few patients survived in fair health for five to ten years; one untreated case had a complete remission for sixteen years and died in her old age of a chest infection.[36] It is not generally realized how much the position is changing every year with regard to the treatment of leukaemia. One expert has recently collected one hundred case records of apparent cure; many patients have had no signs of the disease for ten years.

Multiple sclerosis (MS)

In diseases of the nervous system multiple sclerosis (MS) is the commonest progressive incurable disease. If voluntary euthanasia legislation were ever enacted, this complaint would call for consideration; and indeed it was mentioned by one of the medical contributors to *Euthanasia*.[37] He asked whether it was 'justifiable to prolong such a life' by 'antibiotics and pain-relieving drugs'. Even if most clinicians do not consider that pain-relieving drugs prolong life, the question about antibiotics is still relevant, for they may prevent death from an infection. The question under discussion is however different: it is whether positive steps should be taken to terminate the life of the person who asked for euthanasia because he had multiple sclerosis.

This question is rendered more difficult by the variable character of the disease. Its onset is varied: weakness may occur in an arm or a leg, blindness may appear. Slowly the initial attack clears up, often completely. The large majority of patients have a period of many months, even years of good health before another attack of paralysis occurs. This is often more severe; probably it does not clear up completely and leaves some residual paralysis, often in one of the legs. About one patient in twenty does not appear to get this relapse, or the interval may be very long, up to thirty-seven years. A few never get a second attack and are regarded tentatively as cured.[38]

After the second attack has occurred, others will almost certainly occur, but it is impossible to say when the next one will appear, and how much residual paralysis will accrue. The course of the disease is very variable, ten to twenty years on an average, but in some cases quicker and in some slower. During the earliest attacks there may be considerable doubt about the diagnosis, for laboratory investigations, although usually helpful, may not yield conclusive evidence. It is really the skill of the consultant neurologist who assesses all aspects of the disease that establishes the diagnosis beyond any reasonable doubt. He will communicate the dread diagnosis to the general medical practitioner who looks after the patient.

Towards the end of the long course of the disease the patient is usually confined to bed, severely paralysed, has much shaking of the hands and an indistinct speech. The disease by itself seldom produces pain, but the disability is very severe in the later stages. Frustration must be extremely trying. It is perhaps fortunate that a fair proportion of patients towards the end show signs that the brain is also involved. They become unreasonably euphoric (cheerful) and have some reduction of their mental powers. Some are definitely childish and this mental failure is perhaps merciful.

It is extremely difficult to know when the patient should know the diagnosis, the name of his disease. There seems little point in informing him during the first attack, when the diagnosis may still be uncertain, and a long interval may pass before a second attack establishes the diagnosis. A second attack may never occur. Even when it does it may not be severe, there may be many years yet in which the person may continue to work and carry on a reasonable existence, with little disability and no pain. It is important to preserve hope as long as possible and to boost morale. Possibly a new form of treatment is being tried which will arrest the disease or delay any further recurrence. Sooner or later most patients become acquainted in one way or another with a knowledge of the name of their disease. Then it is only a matter of time until they find out that established multiple sclerosis (MS) is incurable and progressive. Many years however may still elapse during which they may still count life worth living.

If legislation on voluntary euthanasia were ever enacted it must be asked at what stage of the disease the physician in charge of the patient would feel himself under some obligation to tell the person the dread diagnosis and the hopeless prognosis. Should the doctor then press the patient to sign and confirm an advance declaration? Certain arguments could be put forward in favour of this course,

rather than waiting until the disease became far advanced, the patient
only then signing his first request for voluntary euthanasia. He would
then, under the terms of the Voluntary Euthanasia Bill (1969), have to
wait for thirty days before euthanasia could be administered.

Skin diseases

Further examples could be given of 'incurable, irremediable diseases'
of the body, even although most doctors have met, or heard of, some
very startling recovery. Diseases of the skin can be most trying. Some
are incurable. They are disfiguring, they may itch incessantly, they
turn people into social outcasts – the lepers indeed of modern society.
Undoubtedly if voluntary euthanasia legislation were passed, some
dermatological patients would consider whether death were not better
than life. Were they not incurable? Yet some consultant dermatolo-
gists would have misgivings. Bizarre recoveries have occurred such
as:

Case 3. A single woman, aged 29, has been affected since birth with
icthyosis [very large areas of thickened rough skin, resembling that of a
reptile, a permanent condition], covering her neck, shoulders, chest, but-
tocks, limbs ... The patient's father and one sister were similarly affected.
Her attitude was that of the typical 'leper complex'. She was virtually
imprisoned by her condition. She was asked to read a case report of the
successful treatment of a similar condition and she was treated by hypnosis
to induce subjective feelings of changes in the skin. In the third week of
treatment peeling of the skin commenced. Seven weeks later complete
naked-eye remission. Four years later she was still apparently cured.[39]

This report from a medical journal illustrates the impossibility of
declaring any list of skin diseases as incurable.

Injuries of the head and spine

It is natural and right that the general public should be exercised
about some of the results of severe injury either of the head and brain,
or of the spine and spinal cord. A different state of affairs prevailed
in 1929, when I was a Casualty Officer at St Thomas's Hospital. A
man with a head injury in those days was placed quietly in a bed; we
did nothing because we could do nothing helpful. Many of those with
severe head injuries died.

A recent large series of head injuries demonstrated that modern
methods of resuscitation, including the use of the respirator, allowed
some 95% of all persons admitted to hospital for a head injury to
recover completely;[40] 5% did not recover completely and constitute

a medical problem. Thus in this large series of head injury patients 102 patients remained unconscious for more than a month. Out of these some 63 survived, the remainder died. Out of the 63 survivors three quarters were cured and able to work, only about one quarter (15 patients) were unable to do so. These figures should dispel any idea that patients remain in hospital indefinitely. No surgeon wishes to minimize the tragedy of a patient left unconscious for a lengthy period of time, but if he is unconscious he is suffering no pain. Perhaps there is still hope, even for full recovery. No patient remains indefinitely in a respirator if the neurosurgeon, in full consultation with his colleagues, has decided that no useful purpose will be served to prolong measures undertaken originally to resuscitate the patient. His experience, gained even through the tragedies, can be the only factor that aids the decision. No one wishes to minimize the sufferings of the relatives who wait and go on waiting; they suffer, but not the unconscious patient.

Under circumstances such as these it is extremely doubtful if an experienced neurosurgeon would consider legislation on voluntary euthanasia (with or without the advance declaration) as anything but a great embarrassment. Possibly the relatives, if their agreement was sought, would not prove equal to the burden of decision.

Equally tragic are the few people who damage the spinal cord at a very high level (high tetraplegia), especially as this accident often results from diving into a swimming pool. In the whole of England there are some thirty to fifty persons each year who sustain a high tetraplegia. They are completely paralysed in all four limbs (tetraplegia), and may have trouble in passing the urine. The condition is a permanent one, and there is no recovery of any part of the spinal cord that has been destroyed. Cases are of course sent to a special centre for spinal injuries, such as Stoke Mandeville. There expert care and nursing will render life possible for many years. The psychological shock is enormous at first, but surrounded by those who have found a way of life, it is amazing how many rise above a devastating disability. A few even undertake remunerative employment. Presenting the results recently a neurosurgeon stated, 'I can say apart from the early weeks after injury it is rare to find a tetraplegic who does not prefer to be alive.'[41] If legislation were passed on voluntary euthanasia should patients in those first few weeks after the accident, faced with the prospect of permanent complete paralysis in all four limbs, be given the option of death? Would it be a kindness to them or their relatives? If compassion is the queen of the virtues, is there no place for courage as a courtier?

It is not proposed to discuss the incurable disabilities that may follow accidents, whether these occur in motor cars, in industry or even in the home. Many are left with permanent severe defects, limbs are lost or badly damaged, function may be poorly restored and pain may be present for the remainder of the person's life. In some instances litigation about compensation occurs. If someone is left crippled and in pain, unable to return to work, would not this be regarded as qualifying him for voluntary euthanasia? Perhaps this would prove a useful argument to bring about a quick settlement for compensation, if the man was badly damaged, or an increased award to his widow if euthanasia was administered. The injured man would have to consider all this before he decided to try rehabilitation or choose to apply for euthanasia.

Malformed children

Among the list of incurable diseases there are those children who have severe physical or mental defect. In England and Wales about 15,000 mentally defective babies are born each year; about 1 % of all births have some defect of body or mind. The outlook for the less severely defective is good, although their families are under continued strain. During the first few months or years of life it is often impossible to foretell the degree of morbidity even although the nature of the defect is known. The majority live useful lives in childhood and even as adults. 'A small number identifiable at birth or soon after, will never do so.'[42]

Anencephalus (absence of the brain) is the most severe defect of the brain, being present in 2% of all malformed children; spina bifida (malformation of the spine) without anencephalus is present in 2·2% and mongolism (a variety of mental deficiency) in 1·6%. Among the anencephalics over 90% are stillborn and the remainder die within a few days of delivery. In recent years modern surgical treatment has improved the lot of some spina bifida children. This condition is a serious permanent deformity of the spine, causing weakness in the legs and difficulties in controlling the passage of urine. In untreated spina bifida children the outlook is very serious. Thus of those who are born with this deformity, whether alive or stillborn, 10% are alive and well after five years of life, another 10% are disabled and the remainder are dead. Modern surgical treatment can ensure a normal life for only a small number of those who, if untreated, would have died or lived to be disabled. There is therefore much heartsearching among neurosurgeons concerning the evaluation of the results of treatment and the selection of children for this operation. Some may consider that the poor results hardly justify the operation; other surgeons point to a few encouraging successes. In medical circles it is generally recognized that improvement can be obtained only by continued research. They would point to the fact that hydrocephalus, another congenital deformity of the nervous system of infants and one involving the brain, and in the past usually fatal, is now beginning to yield very many successes to modern surgical treatment.

It seems impossible to envisage any easy solution of the problems raised by malformation and mental deficiency. For the families concerned there is continued strain, not only for the parents but for the other children. Care and training of the mentally defective is costly in terms of personnel and in the expenditure involved in training and education. There are so many different varieties that it is impossible to generalize. A few categories are known to the general public, such as the over-active mongols, who often seem in their own way to be so carefree. Spastics form a large group, some of whom improve remarkably if the right intensive training is given from an early age. Some spastics are remarkably intelligent persons, even though they may have difficulty in moving their limbs smoothly or in speaking normally. A great friend of mine is a spastic and a highly intelligent person; he was only prevented from being ordained because he could not hold the chalice steadily.

It is extremely difficult to envisage the repercussions of legislation for voluntary euthanasia on the malformed child and the mentally defective child. The Voluntary Euthanasia Society of England has never advocated termination of life of malformed infants at birth, or during childhood. Legislation proposed by them has excluded all minors, whatever their condition. This however does not eliminate the problem which would arise when these minors, having incurable physical or mental defects, became adults on their eighteenth birthday. Should a bad case of spina bifida, who has not responded well to all forms of treatment, then be offered the chance to choose voluntary euthanasia? Among the spastics, the same question would arise. Will some spastics be found of sufficient mental maturity to qualify for the choice of voluntary euthanasia? Will others be deemed to be

mentally unfit to choose voluntary euthanasia and be denied its so-
called mercy? With improved care a higher proportion of mental
defectives will reach adult life, with an incurable psychological defect.
If they then develop another serious incurable disease, such as cancer,
what legislation is envisaged to cover their alleged needs for mercy-
killing?

Uncertainty in diagnosis

In addressing the doctors who attended one of the few symposia on
euthanasia Lord Cohen, President of the General Medical Council,
said, 'Practising doctors must know of many cases in which death
seemed inevitable yet the patient made a good recovery.'[43] It follows
that in each of these patients, doctors had considered that death was
inevitable because of four separate facts. First, diagnosis: there was
accurate knowledge about the diseases present in the body. Secondly,
the patient: there was good information about the physique of the
person who had developed these diseases. Thirdly, prognosis: there
was a clear idea about the outcome of the diseases in a person of this
physique. Fourthly, the person was apparently near to death. He was
apparently in the terminal stages of illness. In ordinary English, he
was a dying person. There would have been sufficient evidence to
have administered voluntary euthanasia under the terms proposed in
the Voluntary Euthanasia Bill, 1969. Yet Lord Cohen stated, the
patient did not die, instead he 'made a good recovery'.

It is currently considered that doctors can diagnose disease with
comparative certainty. All estimates of the prognosis, of whether the
condition is curable or incurable, all ideas concerning the outcome of
the disease and whether death must be feared, rest on the basis of a
firm diagnosis. It is right that doctors should ask that the general
public trust them in all their decisions. There is little purpose in venti-
lating any misgivings about the accuracy of the diagnosis in a public
discussion. It is best for doctors to discuss these matters in private. In
fact they are continually doing this, thereby improving the accuracy
of the diagnosis. The discussion that follows is necessitated by those
who consider that a consultant and a general medical practitioner can
'certify in writing that the patient appears to them to be suffering
from an irremediable disease, . . . that is, a serious physical illness
thought in the patient's case to be incurable and expected to cause
him severe distress' – these were the relevant words from the Voluntary Euthanasia Bill, 1969.

From time to time doubts are expressed by the General Register Office about the accuracy of the causes of death as stated on the death certificate. In 1966 a special investigation was held into the matter by two doctors.[44]

It should be remembered that before voluntary euthanasia could be administered a consultant and a physician would have to 'certify in writing that the patient appears to them to be suffering from an irremediable complaint'. This important certificate would rely on the accuracy of the diagnosis of two doctors before euthanasia was administered and presumably in certain cases there would be a post-mortem examination after death had occurred. This would occur fairly frequently in the larger hospitals, especially the teaching hospitals, because this more than any other procedure leads to advances in medical knowledge and diagnostic skill.

In the investigation conducted by the General Register Office in 1966 the clinical staff of seventy-five selected hospitals were asked to fill in dummy death certificates of all persons who died during a period of six consecutive months. These certificates were filled up by the clinical staff as soon as the patient had died, and certainly before they had seen the results of the subsequent post-mortem examination. Disagreement between the dummy certificates of the supposed cause of death written by the clinical staff and the final certificates of the actual causes of death, detected by the pathologist at the post-mortem examination, was present in rather more than 50% of the returns.

The clinicians had all the clinical facts, the results of the X-rays, the examination of blood and other specimens. Sometimes the diagnosis was uncertain even when the patient died, but in others the clinicians were 'fairly certain'. Clinicians indeed were asked to say if they were 'fairly certain' about the diseases causing death, but even then there was disagreement with the causes of death as detected by the pathologist at post-mortem examination in some 44% of the cases.

Mistakes might be those of commission or of omission. Thus a substantial proportion of deaths ascribed by the clinicians to haemorrhage in the brain (cerebral haemorrhage) and other forms of disease of the blood vessels of the brain (cerebral thrombosis and embolism) – all of which cause the patient to suffer from a stroke – were found to be errors of commission, death being due to other causes. This also applied to the clinical diagnosis of death due to pneumonia or diabetes, for the pathologist found other causes at the post-mortem examination. There had also been errors of omission by the clinicians.

According to the facts found by the pathologists at the post-mortem examination the clinicians during life had failed to record 50% of the bile-duct (biliary) cancers, 33% of the tuberculosis, bronchitis and bronchicetases and nearly 20% of the lung cancers and peptic ulcers.

Those who are not medically qualified should not read too much into these disquietening figures. Patients who die in hospital, especially if they are elderly, usually have more than one complaint. It is not generally realized that serious disease such as cancer or tuberculosis may occur, and eventually prove fatal, but cause very few symptoms and no pain during life. It is not generally recognized how much one disease may resemble another so that diagnosis is always difficult in an internal complaint. On the other hand one cannot disregard these figures, which demonstrate a large gap between the knowledge of the clinician and the facts as detected by a pathologist at post-mortem. But it is one thing to make a clinical diagnosis as a basis of treatment and a totally different matter to certify this disease as a reason for euthanasia. As long as the patient lives there is an opportunity to revise the diagnosis and the treatment, and if an incurable complaint has been diagnosed incorrectly the patient may recover to confound the prognosis and demand a revision of the diagnosis. Had voluntary euthanasia been administered after all reasonable care had been employed by the doctor, what would be his position if the post-mortem revealed a significant discrepancy? Could aggrieved relatives sue for damages or negligence? As far as the doctor is concerned, it is one thing to have one's patient die of natural causes and one's fallibility exposed at the post-mortem examination, for this often occurs; it is a totally different matter to feel that these mistakes resulted in the termination of life by euthanasia.

Medical science is committed to a search for scientific truth, it is dedicated to correction of its own fallibilities. If legislation on voluntary euthanasia were ever enacted there would be one investigation after another, especially at the teaching hospitals, to determine the measure of agreement between the diseases certified by the consultant and the second doctor during the life of the patient and those detected at the post-mortem examination after the administration of euthanasia.

The foregoing refers to deaths which occur in hospital. In Britain over 50% of deaths occur at home. Few of these patients have been investigated as adequately as those who die in hospital, though some of course have been investigated in hospital but have returned home because this seemed the best to all concerned. There has been no investigation of the accuracy of diagnosis of general medical practitioners who work under the difficult conditions of caring for a sick person in his own home. If legislation on voluntary euthanasia were enacted, it is considered that few consultants would certify the presence of an incurable, fatal disease, unless full investigation of the patient could be undertaken in hospital. If the patient had been in hospital recently the consultant might feel reasonably certain; in other instances it would be necessary to admit the patient from his home to the hospital for full investigation with a view to administering euthanasia. If there were no beds in the public hospital available, the question would arise whether special nursing homes could not undertake this task. Nursing homes might arise which would specialize in this work, especially if the patient was able to overcome the financial obstacles. This has occurred in the termination of pregnancy; indeed women have come from foreign countries for this purpose. Whether this would occur in voluntary euthanasia would depend on the legislation enacted and might be influenced by the question of fees, especially if these were large, for it would prove possible to have them charged to the estate, and there need be no post-mortem examination, either, to trouble either mind or conscience; like corpse or ashes, they would be 'AT REST'.

Errors of observation

Observer error occurs in all branches of medicine and surgery, because doctors fail to observe facts accurately. It is notoriously difficult to measure blood pressure accurately; it tends to rise when the patient becomes anxious, such as occurs when the patient sees the doctor. Two doctors recently wrote a paper entitled 'Observer error in cardiology' (diseases of the heart). They mentioned the many difficulties in interpreting the electrocardiogram (electrical tracing of the heart); the errors, assessed at some 17%, in the diagnosis of angina (one form of coronary heart disease), and the 'very great observer error' in detecting the ankle pulse.[45]

Accuracy of diagnosis improves with every new method of investigation. The electrocardiogram has made the diagnosis of coronary heart disease possible; radiology has improved enormously the accuracy of the diagnosis of diseases of the stomach. Neither is infallible. An effort was made at the Leeds General Infirmary[46] to establish

the precise diagnosis in 200 consecutive patients in whom a surgeon
had performed a partial gastrectomy (removal of part of the stomach).
This operation is usually performed to cure a gastric ulcer or remove
a gastric cancer. Before the operation a physician had examined the
patient, and a consultant radiologist had reported on the X-ray. After
the operation a pathologist reported on the disease present in the
portion of stomach removed by the surgeon, and thus established the
final diagnosis. In cancer of the stomach the physician had made a
correct diagnosis in only 35 % of cases, the radiologist in some 80 %.
(Naturally before the operation the physician and surgeon both receive the report from the radiologist and amend their tentative diagnosis accordingly.) Even the radiologist missed 20 % of the cancers,
although he found something abnormal and this confirmed the decision to operate, thus establishing the correct diagnosis. In diseases in
which radiology is of little help and no operation is performed there
may be much more uncertainty. An elderly person who is thought to
have had a stroke is an obvious example, as there are many different
diseases which may cause a patient to become unconscious and many
varieties of stroke, and again, as he is unconscious, it is impossible to
examine the nervous system adequately. Thus a tumour in the brain
might be silent until suddenly it precipitated a stroke; pneumonia
may be almost silent, yet early on cause the patient to become unconscious, so that a stroke is feared.

Uncertainty in prognosis

Even if the diagnosis of an incurable, fatal disease has been established on a firm basis there is great difficulty in determining the
expectation of life that the patient may enjoy. That is to say there is
uncertainty over the prognosis.

Prognosis would appear to be more certain in a steadily progressive disease such as occurs when cancer has spread far and wide in
the body as metastases. But there are many uncertainties, and a doctor who gives a patient 'three months to live' will usually prove
wrong. It is impossible to number dates in this manner, although a
wise clinician might estimate 'a few months, say from three to six'.

Even in the last stage of cancer all sorts of unpredictable events
may occur. One of the deep-treated tumours may rupture an artery,
so that the patient dies rapidly from an internal haemorrhage. No
blood may be lost from the body and the rapid death may be

unexplained unless a post-mortem examination is performed. Pneumonia and other infections may occur silently leading to a rapid deterioration. All this may occur while the narcotic drugs are being increased in order to give relief from pain; should death then occur it is difficult, if not impossible, to say how much this was produced by widespread cancer, infections, haemorrhage and the high dosage of narcotics and other drugs. Prognosis, even in the last stages of slowly progressive disease, such as widespread cancer, is often uncertain.

The prognosis in other diseases may be far more difficult. The doctor just has to wait on events. It is extremely difficult to say what will be the outcome of an attack of coronary thrombosis until several days have passed and the danger of complications is over. Prognosis is notoriously uncertain in someone who has had a cerebral vascular accident (stroke) and is unconscious. Some unconscious patients die within a matter of hours or days, others make a complete recovery, others recover only partially. Doubtless some who recover wish they had died and it would be but natural for certain relatives to feel the same, at least at times, especially if the patient is left speechless and paralysed.

It is only to be expected that the pathetic picture of someone permanently paralysed and possibly speechless should figure prominently in the literature of those who support legislation on voluntary euthanasia.[47] In certain of these patients the loss of speech might make it difficult for them to make their wishes known; others have some reduction of their mental powers and might be unable to make an informed rational decision. The advance declaration for voluntary euthanasia is designed to meet this contingency. Whether the patient had enough mental powers to confirm or to revoke his advance declaration is a matter that would exercise many and for which there would be no easy answer.

Even if a disease has been correctly diagnosed and the extent and severity of the disease has been accurately assessed, it would still be difficult to give a precise prognosis. A disease occurs in someone's body and bodies differ. Everyone is conscious that faces differ and that no two faces are the same, unless they are those of identical twins. The internal organs also differ in structure, composition and in the genetic code imprinted in every cell of the body. The same disease will always be different in two different patients. It is difficult to generalize about the outcome of illness in different people.

It has always been known that people resist disease in different

ways. Sometimes this seems obvious, as when an aged person suc-
cumbs to pneumonia, whereas a young robust adult will soon overcome the disease. It is however usually quite impossible to say how
well a person will contend with cancer, or a coronary attack, or a
stroke. Physique enters into all these matters in ways which cannot at
present be determined at a clinical examination. How any one person
will 'stand up' to a long illness like diabetes or multiple sclerosis is
therefore uncertain.

Another source of uncertainty which is common in middle age, and
universal in the elderly, is the presence of many different diseases in
the same person. Many of these complaints produce no symptoms,
most of them are not suspected by the patient. They will be found
only at a comprehensive clinical examination. Several of them are
completely silent and can only be detected at a post-mortem examination.[48] Thus at post-mortems conducted in Aberdeen, persons dying
in a geriatric unit were found on an average to have six different
physical disorders of the body.[49] This is one of the reasons for the
disagreement between the diseases recorded by the clinician before
death and the catalogue of complaints discovered by the pathologist
at the post-mortem.[50] It is however this comprehensive catalogue of
complaints that was eventually responsible for death. Thus unsuspected coronary artery disease may perhaps be found to be the cause
of sudden death a week after the person had a stroke. A symptomless
cancer of the bile-ducts may explain why the person suffering from
senile dementia became seriously confused in his speech, ate no food
and died much more rapidly than expected.

The last illness and the terminal stage

People differ and their deaths differ; no two deaths are identical.
There are many surprises, often many ups and downs before the
terminal stage is reached. Having said that, it is still possible to talk
about certain patterns of dying. Death may come rapidly; people are
then said to 'collapse suddenly'. A man may die suddenly in the
prime of life, if he has a severe heart attack of coronary thrombosis.
A middle-aged man may rapidly become unconscious and die in a
few hours if he has a cerebral haemorrhage. An elderly woman may
be sitting quietly in her chair, she is here one moment and gone the
next; sudden calm death comes easily in the aged.

Quick painless death seems an easy exit for the person concerned, but it may cause severe and prolonged bereavement among those who are left, especially if it occurred quite unexpectedly in the prime of life. This is not so if it is an elderly person who dies; death has been expected, it is a merciful release. Sudden death at the end of a long painful illness, such as may occur in cancer, or in someone severely paralysed for many years, may be an occasion for thanksgiving.

Other illnesses do not plunge suddenly into a fatal collapse but they pursue an erratic course. Some illnesses are mild and may never threaten life; thus bronchitis may return each winter but clears up each summer. A man comes to disregard another attack of chest trouble, but in a few people, especially those who have smoked many cigarettes, even attacks of bronchitis may become serious.

Other illnesses may be serious even from the very beginning; perhaps even the worst is feared, but then again the patient rallies and appears to make a good recovery. The doctor may know that the patient is not completely cured and often the patient himself realizes that he is not quite the man that he was. As we get older we do not shake off illness as easily as when we were young. Further attacks may occur and possibly this time the patient does not recover quickly or completely. Then in an unpredictable and erratic manner the disease pursues its vacillating but downward course. The patient meanwhile often remains hopeful, for he has rallied many times. Then comes perhaps the final severe attack, terminating in sudden collapse, and the battle is lost. In others a severe attack marches slowly to its appointed end.

Almost everyone can recall hearing of some elderly person who had heart failure, but survived for many months or years, while the disease ran a vacillating course. At times rest in bed was essential and the patient was very ill. Possibly the worst was feared and the family came to pay their last call. Unexpectedly he rallied, responded to treatment, got up once more; he laughed at death and definitely enjoyed life. Other elderly people who suffer heart failure have a long intractable wearisome illness before death comes.

A stroke lays a man low; often however there is a degree of recovery, perhaps not complete, but sufficient to allow a reasonable existence for several years. Others, alas, are bedridden. Then another attack may occur and this may be fatal. Some have several attacks in an unpredictable manner.

In all illnesses that run an erratic or vacillating course it would prove very difficult to know how the patient would respond to the possibility of voluntary euthanasia. Some who would have had many months or years of reasonable health before them might choose death. Others may feel that euthanasia would have saved someone who was bedridden after a stroke from many years of misery. Certainly it would often relieve the feelings and physical burdens of relatives who were called to nurse them; but more information is required about the true desires of someone who has had a severe stroke. Many such people have some failure of their mental powers, others have difficulty in talking, so that it would sometimes be difficult to know if they can make an informed and valid application for voluntary euthanasia.

Then again certain diseases seem to march fairly steadily forward until death occurs. Thus there are a few rare neurological complaints in which paralysis slowly spreads over the body. Actually in most of these there are times when the patient deteriorates more rapidly, in others he is holding his own. Eventually however he may be unable to move hand or foot, speech may be lost, swallowing becomes difficult, breathing is laboured. Life can be indeed a grievous burden.

If people were asked to mention a disease which marches relentlessly forward, many would name cancer. This is by no means correct; for the initial tumour surgery, with or without radiotherapy, may even complete the cure. If recurrences occur it may not be until many years have passed; often they are painless and the person may die without suspecting that he has had a return of his cancer. In a minority of patients the recurrences of cancer at many sites in the body are painful, even extremely painful. Even then further surgical measures, or radiotherapy, or some new drug may overcome the various tumour masses, so that pain is decreased, or completely relieved. Other patients have painful recurrences, not amenable to treatment, and the doctors rely on analgesic and narcotic drugs to deaden pain, even if cure no longer proves possible. It is in diseases such as this, those which march relentlessly forward and for which cure is now a remote possibility, that some would consider that voluntary euthanasia might offer a path of mercy. Here the psychological reactions of someone dying of cancer are of prime importance. These are discussed in detail in the next chapter; the choice of voluntary euthanasia will also be considered there.

There are many patterns of dying, but it is possible to speak of three broad categories: (i) rapid dying, often unexpected; (ii) unpredictable dying, with much vacillation and many surprises; (iii) steady, slow dying, such as may occur in certain progressive diseases. Owing to the fact that death comes in a thousand different ways it is almost impossible to give any definition of the term 'terminal illness'. An easy practical definition is that it is the last illness, but no one knows for certain that it is the last illness until the doctor writes the death certificate. Terminal illness is the illness from which a man dies, but it is by no means always possible to say when someone goes into hospital for the last time. Will it be the last time?

Those who support legislation on voluntary euthanasia speak of 'terminal illness', even 'terminal patients',[51] but they never define the term. At one time we were content to speak of dying patients and fatal illness, but the phrase 'terminal illness' has crept into the literature in recent years as one of those euphemisms that are used to cover up the reality of death. When Dr Exton-Smith[52] made his pioneer studies in 'terminal illness' in the elderly, he meant their last illness, the illness for which they were admitted to the geriatric unit and from which they in fact died. Critically ill patients who were admitted to the ward and in whom death was anticipated, but who subsequently recovered and were discharged, were not listed among those who had a 'terminal illness'. In actual practice a doctor will only make a tentative diagnosis of 'terminal illness' when he has reached a decision that death is reasonably certain.

This all-important decision of the doctor that the patient is in the last stages of some fatal illness is of crucial importance. Previously the doctor has striven to defeat the disease process or impede its advance, or at least arrest its ravages; he has aimed at making life as full and worth-while an experience as possible. One remedy after another is tried and fresh investigations suggest new lines of attack. Even if he cannot destroy the disease at the centre, he may still perhaps check its advances at the periphery. In all this most patients will co-operate as long as there are grounds for hope. There may not be much hope for full recovery, but perhaps there may be months or weeks of reasonable existence left. The doctor watches the many signs that monitor the march of the disease. The day, perhaps the hour, comes when the scales move suddenly under the weight of evidence and the doctor realizes that the battle is lost. In his mind there forms the idea that the patient is dying. He is going to lose the patient. Death is inevitable and usually it is near at hand. The patient now enters the terminal stage of his last illness.

The phrase 'terminal stage' of the last illness has a clearly defined

medical connotation, whereas the term 'terminal illness' is meaning-
less except in retrospect. It was in the former sense that a recent text-
book on geriatrics spoke of the treatment in the terminal stages:

> . . . the later stages of progressive diseases which have a reasonably pre-
> dictable end, even though they may be slow in coming. Cancer, intractable
> heart failure, progressive pulmonary (lung) or renal (kidney) insufficiency,
> amongst others, present themselves so in geriatric wards . . . The time for
> active curative treatment is past; so probably is any temptation to the
> physician to use antibiotics against chest infection.[53]

Symptoms are treated to relieve discomfort, but not to cure. Thus the
bowels must be relieved if constipation is severe, the bladder must be
emptied if this is no longer possible, the mouth must receive attention
lest it become dry and painful. Fluids must be given, probably intravenously, because this will relieve thirst and prevent the mouth from
becoming dry. No attempts at resuscitation should be contemplated.[54]
At this, the terminal stage of a fatal illness, the only relevant treatment is the relief of distress. Often sedatives are given so that the
patient is completely peaceful; narcotics may be given liberally to
secure complete relief of pain.

Sociologists who observe and record all that happens to a dying
patient in hospital have spoken of this as one of the critical junctures
of illness. It separates curative from palliative medicine. Before this
stage there were still some grounds for hope, even if the patient was
sufficiently ill to be on the danger list. Once on this danger list the
nearest of kin has been informed, but now the patient has been put
into a completely different category: he is in the terminal stage, he is
about to die. American sociologists have noted that at this critical
juncture: (1) The patient is defined by the staff as dying. (2) Staff and
family prepare for his death, as does perhaps the patient. (3) There is
'nothing more to do' to prevent death. The final descent into death
may take hours or days, even longer, but, it ends in (4) the last hours
of watching and death itself.[55] At all stages nurses, doctors and others
can do much to help both the person who is dying and the relatives
and friends. This relieves distress, it defeats loneliness. Respect is
demonstrated, compassion is shewn. It is terrible and it is wrong even
to say, 'Nothing more can be done'.

The decision that death is inevitable, as far as clinician can reasonably judge, may occur relatively early in slow progressive disease.
Intractable heart failure in an elderly person, and advanced spreading
cancer are two of the best known examples. Since widespread cancer

in a certain proportion of persons can be very painful, unless well relieved by narcotic drugs, it is necessary to discuss it in some detail. Considerable hesitation is felt at introducing this subject in this book lest it arouses anxieties, but the public are exercised over this problem in any consideration of voluntary euthanasia. Moreover, certain allegations have been made that doctors are performing euthanasia in a clandestine manner on some of the patients who are suffering pain due to widespread recurrences of cancer. These allegations seldom contain any details. Certain cases at least, in my opinion, are founded on a misapprehension about the dosage of morphine – a point to be discussed immediately.

It should be clearly recognized that we are discussing the case of someone suffering from widespread incurable metastases of cancer. The earlier stages of the disease, when curative methods could be adopted, are past. At a later stage palliative measures may have been attempted to check the spread of the disease, even if complete cure was no longer possible. These measures might decrease the size of certain tumours, even cause their disappearance, so that pressure on nerves and other structures would have been relieved. Eventually however in certain patients the stage is reached when the doctors decide that nothing more curative can be done. The patient passes the critical juncture, as it has been called, and the doctors decide that the terminal stage has come, even if as in widespread cancer there are still some weeks of life left. Death is inevitable. Henceforth treatment is directed to the relief of pain, discomfort and mental distress. A great deal can be done to improve the quality of life even in the terminal stage of this incurable disease. Henceforth it is the quality of life and not its quantity, which demands the attention of all concerned. No one knows how long life will be, although mental estimates are often made. They remain guesses and any discussion of the so-called shortening of life becomes almost an academic exercise.

At this terminal stage mental peace and the relief of pain are the outstanding needs. It seems foolish to deny any patient the relief that narcotic drugs offer through foolish fears of drug addiction or problematical considerations that the drug may shorten life. On the contrary, one consultant physician with great experience has stated that if injections of morphine, or some similar narcotic drug are given correctly, so that pain is relieved, a patient may actually live longer.[56] Relieved of pain, the patient may eat better and sleep better, both means of conserving the patient's strength. Other physicians consider that narcotic drugs in large dosage may perhaps shorten life, but only by a short period of time. Since no one can predict the hour of death, any shortening of life remains problematical in degree and uncertain in extent. Injections may be given regularly by day and by night, and they tend to be given in increasing amounts as the illness progresses. The patient will eventually die within a few hours of the last injection. It cannot be otherwise; but he does not die because of the last injection.

It is difficult to define the fatal toxic dose of a narcotic drug in any patient who has been receiving regular injections for a fair period of time. Doctors who are unaware of this, and note that a patient died soon after the dose of the injection was increased, may fear, quite incorrectly, that they were actually responsible for death. They may even feel that this amounted to euthanasia. I was sometimes troubled thus myself when in practice. If the full record of injections and all the post-mortem findings were to be presented to a panel of medical experts, it is certain that these fears would, almost always, prove without medical foundation. Progressive cancer, complicated by infection, and some collapse of the heart and circulation may all have contributed to the death. It may be decided by the experts that the large doses of narcotic drugs, administered in dosage adequate to control the pain, played no part in the total causation of death.

The patient may become physiologically dependent on the narcotic drug, but physiological dependence (called addiction) seldom occurs if the drug is started by the mouth and increased gradually if necessary in order to control the pain. It is often necessary to resort to injections when the pain becomes severe or drugs can no longer be taken by mouth. Addiction to the drug need not occur if narcotics and other drugs in combination with them are used skilfully. It is important that recently qualified doctors should receive special instruction, theoretical and practical, in these matters, possibly at some specialized unit for terminal care, since this type of patient seldom stays long at a teaching hospital.

Preparations by mouth are used at first, such as the Brompton cocktail, a mixture of morphine or diamorphine (heroin), a small dose of cocaine and alcohol. Sedatives by themselves will not relieve pain, but promote sleep. They relieve anxiety but are often unnecessary. Various new synthetic analgesics such as pentazocine (Fortral), methadone or levorphanol (Dromoran) or phenazocine (Narphen) may help. Treated thus, pain can be controlled even in terminal cases of widespread cancer. If pain is severe, injections of a narcotic drug are usually given. In the correct dosage, repeated at the appropriate interval, they can control pain, even if severe. Morphine is still preferred by many; heroin (diamorphine) is a valuable alternative, likewise omnopon.

If morphine or heroin injections are given frequently, tolerance may develop in four to eight weeks. It may then be necessary in some, but by no means all patients, to increase the dose in order to alleviate the pain to the same degree. In the meantime disease has possibly spread to other parts of the body and existing tumours have increased in size so that there is more pain. It is often difficult, if not impossible, to say whether the dose of morphine is increased because there is more pain or because of increased tolerance. Those with the greatest experience of these drugs, such as the doctors who work in special units for cancer patients, state emphatically that moderate doses of narcotics, if given regularly at the correct interval of time, offer good relief to the pain in advanced cancer. All pain has a big psychological aspect and patients who have confidence in their treatment seldom need the large dosage employed by some doctors.

When patients are treated at home, or in institutions where there is a shortage of nursing and medical staff, large dosage of narcotics may be employed, but this is not so satisfactory. Occasionally it is difficult to secure regular injections at frequent intervals and then the dose may be pushed up rapidly.

Fears have been entertained that morphine injections, even if correctly given, in large doses in the treatment of advanced cancer, often shorten life by causing a fatal respiratory depression. This is not correct, although even the smallest dose of morphine (10 mgs.) tends to make breathing slow and shallow, influencing the respiratory centre in the brain, but not in a dangerous manner. The fatal dose of morphine in a normal healthy person has been assessed as 250 mgs. by one British authority[57] but 250-500 mgs. by another American authority.[58] This means that the accepted fatal dose of morphine in a normal person is some twenty-five to fifty times the recommended minimal dose, and some twelve to twenty-five times the recommended maximal dose of 20 mgs.

Another point which is not generally recognized is that, when the dose of morphine is increased gradually to combat pain, starting with the normal minimal injection of 10 mgs. and rising slowly to 20 mgs. after a few weeks, and eventually to even a higher dose, habituation to the drug has occurred, so that the higher dose not only produces the same effect as the normal dose on the pain, but *at the same time produces the same effect on the respiratory centre.*

Some who support legislation on voluntary euthanasia have stated, quite incorrectly, that a doctor is often faced with an impossible dilemma in the care of cancer patients. They state that a doctor must either increase the morphine and thus kill the patient by respiratory depression or leave the patient unrelieved of his pain owing to increased tolerance. These statements occurred in the first medical book on voluntary euthanasia, where Dr Killick Millard, a medical officer of health, and not a clinician, pictured a doctor on the brink of a precipice – one step forward, one slight increase in the dose of morphine, and the patient would be killed. If however, the dose of morphine was not increased, the pain would not be controlled. The story has been handed down in the literature of voluntary euthanasia. Thus Glanville Williams wrote, 'The logic of morphine and other like drugs is sooner or later to present a choice between administering what is likely to be a fatal dose and leaving the patient without relief'. . . . having preceded this statement on the same page by the statement that 'a grain of morphine might for ordinary persons be a fatal dose'.[59] While it cannot be asserted that someone in apparent health could never be killed by double the normal dose of morphine, or for that matter aspirin, it must be stated that doctors have to work on what usually occurs within the wide range of those who are considered normal, and that the normal toxic, that is fatal, dose of morphine is some twelve to twenty-five times the recommended maximal dose and some four to eight times the figure of one grain cited by Glanville Williams.

It should be added that doctors are not taught to carry in their heads the toxic dose of any drug; they consult an authoritative book. Doctors are taught the minimal and maximal dose of the drugs that they employ. Thus, at a recent debate on voluntary euthanasia at one of the London teaching hospitals, the author challenged the audience of some eighty doctors and medical students to say whether any of them knew the toxic dose of morphine. No one volunteered, and many appeared to be surprised when the figure and the authorities were cited.

All this is not to deny that morphine, like any other powerful drug, should always be given with caution. Thus even the normal dose might hamper the breathing of someone who had too much fluid within the lungs and the bronchial tubes. This could become serious, especially if an infection such as pneumonia was threatening. The same is true even of the most harmless drugs, and no doctor would prescribe even one tablet of aspirin to anyone who had recently vomited blood, for it might provoke a fatal haemorrhage.

Finally it is difficult, if not impossible, to decide what is the fatal toxic dose of morphine in a person who has severe physical pain, because pain is one of the best antidotes to the sedative action of morphine.

Considerable attention has been paid to the terminal stages of cancer when accompanied by severe pain, but it must be emphasized that most cancer patients die peacefully in their sleep and that only a minority have severe pain in the last stages of their disease. Many, probably the majority, suffer little or no pain when recurrences occur.

It must also be emphasized once more that it is impossible to divide the pain of cancer, or any other disease, into two portions, physical pain arising in the body and psychological pain and distress in the mind. Some of the pain in cancer is psychological in origin, and it is unfortunate that we have to conceptualize pain into two halves, pain of the body and pain in the mind. The only one to feel pain is a person who has a body and mind inextricably joined.

Dying

The terminal stage of mortal illness ends in dying, a process which may be swift but is often slow. Years ago the dying patient was often conscious until almost the last hour of life, he would be seen propped up in bed, surrounded by nearest members of his family, speaking his last farewells, even uttering famous last words. This can be very dramatic, but many find the experience too disturbing. Others however often find the experience helps them; some of the last memories of their relative are very precious, even if poignant. Dying may be a slow business, no one expects that it will last as long as it sometimes does. Some nurses find the whole procedure very traumatic and hope it will end soon. Doctors too find it difficult to accept the death of their patient; it is the apparent defeat of all their clinical skill. This is not so; very much can be done to ease the last moments of life. This is also much appreciated by the relatives.

Nowadays most patients in the terminal stage of illness are unconscious. The disease process is severe and gaining the upper hand; this by itself may produce stupor or even loss of consciousness. If the patient appears to be restless, and even distressed, and certainly if there is any hint of pain, large doses of narcotic and sedative drugs are given so that the patient is often unconscious. Modern man can be assured that he will not die in pain. Equally important is the fact that the relatives see that their loved one is free of pain, sleeping peacefully, even unconscious. So they sit by in waiting rooms, or walk the corridors of the hospital, just occasionally going back to the bedside, where perhaps one or two are watching.

Long before this stage is reached there has been the time when, often barely conscious, the patient said perhaps the last farewells, for most people know that they are dying, even if they can never put this into words. Possibly there have been some ministrations of a religious character. As the mind becomes progressively more dim, it is the doctors and nurses who increasingly decide matters, but they keep faith with the patient, explaining everything to him. They continue to talk to him, for he can certainly hear long after he has lost the power of speech. He knows he is not alone; both relatives and doctors and nurses go with him into the valley of the shadow of death.

No patient could discuss euthanasia at this stage; he has not the mental ability to grasp the situation. So the nurses and doctors carry on, informing the relatives that everything possible is being done, that there is no pain; he is unconscious now but still alive. Not dead yet; someone stays by until the end. He died in peace and fell asleep. They say 'A good death', *euthanatos*, in the literal sense of the word as a natural event, not euthanasia wherein one person kills another.

Before the present era of heavy sedation of the dying, it was more common for patients to remain conscious until almost the end. Usually there was some warning a few days or hours before death and the experienced nurse recognized the signs. The classical *facies Hippocratica* might be seen to appear: the eyes half closed, the mouth open, the breathing often noisy, even terribly rattling. The patient usually lay prostrate on his back, or had been sat up in bed to help his breathing. Unless sedated, a person will see and hear long after he lost the power of speech. The eyes may continue to speak recognition, even appreciation, long after the lips are silent. By this time everyone is praying that the act of dying may be as short as possible. No one argues any longer whether this idea is morbid or whether this is permissible in the eyes of the law. No one asks whether drugs have played too active a part, either in prolonging life, or shortening life.

Most are relieved that the patient is sufficiently sedated so that few death agonies are seen. 'It was peaceful at the last, a good death, *euthanatos*', they say as they leave the room.

Incredible as it may seem, people who have been able to record their feelings in the hour of death, doctors who have watched the process with keen eyes and an understanding heart, insist that the last period of conscious life is completely free of pain.[60] There is indeed often a period, by no means short, of perfect peace and some have described a spiritual state that partakes of ecstasy.

William Hunter, the famous anatomist and surgeon, retained his consciousness to the end, having suffered much from painful bouts of angina of the heart. He whispered, 'If I had strength enough to hold a pen, I would write how easy and pleasant a thing it is to die.' All those who have been resuscitated after drowning insist that the last moments of consciousness were not dominated by terrible feelings of suffocation, but that they had no pain at all.

Finally, it must once more be emphasized that in the best terminal care units the period of unconsciousness is usually short, often a matter of a few hours, so that patient and relatives can converse together as long as possible.

V

Psychological Aspects

Relatives of the dying person

Relatives and friends visit the dying person, supporting him in his loneliness, his distress and his dependence. They have their inner grief, for already they have been admitted to the secret that the patient will die. They must start the task of mourning, but this they must hide as far as possible from the loved one, for often he has as yet not realized his fate. This introduces an element of constraint into all their talk. They meet but cannot talk; they talk but cannot meet. How long can they keep up the pretence with someone with whom before they shared so many secrets? If dying is protracted, accompanied by pain, distress of mind and despondent spirits, the relatives carry an almost intolerable burden. The waiting seems without end.

If legislation on voluntary euthanasia were enacted it would prove desirable for the doctor to secure the approval of the relatives before any administration; he would wish to avoid any dispute after the euthanasia. Some legislation on this matter has even envisaged an administrative machinery to hear any objections of the relatives.

In any case relatives would often wish to confer with the patient to ascertain if there was an informed, valid and determined decision to die. They would like to form their own impressions that he was in full possession of his faculties, because a desire for death is sometimes a sign of a psychiatric disorder, called depression. Any discussion with the dying person would be hedged with constraint, a dark area of uncertainty illuminated as yet by the imagination of no playwright, investigated as yet by little sociological research, omitted from all television coverage. All this has yet to come. Who will approach the dying person and act as spokesman for the family? Is it kindness to encourage early death? Kindness to whom – to him lying on the bed or to us sitting on the chairs? What does he really know? Is he choosing death to relieve us? Can we agree to this? Are we not mean to refuse his self-sacrifice? There is room for endless double-talk and double-think in all this. Perhaps the relatives are not all of one mind, and the patient flutters from one mood to another. Perhaps all the motives are of the highest order, perhaps not, for then other more mundane motives obtrude, or are considered to obtrude. There is the inheritance and perhaps a protracted illness is eating into it. After death by voluntary euthanasia had been administered there would probably be a second round of talks among the members of the family, illuminated perhaps for the first time by the knowledge of the clauses of the last will and testament. There might even have been an autopsy examination. This, like the will, might disclose some surprises. Relatives might seek to find consolation in justifying their decisions, others might be confirmed in their disagreement.

The movement to provide legislation for voluntary euthanasia stems largely from the painful memories of friends and relatives. A typical story told by Glanville Williams, described a 'dear friend of mine who died of cancer of the bowel', who spent the last months of his life with pain deadened by morphine, but there was much vomiting. Thus he continued in an 'artificial twilight existence' with extreme restlessness and depression. Understandably Williams asked himself whether 'the unintelligent brutality of such an existence is to be imposed on one who wishes to end it',[1] and complained very truthfully that this question had never been answered by those who oppose legislation on voluntary euthanasia. It is certainly a question which the medical profession must take to heart. If they do not, whether they like it or not, legislation to provide for this contingency may well be enacted. It demands an answer: so read on.

As a preliminary one would like to ask the professor whether another medical opinion, a change of drugs, or even a transfer to another institution might not have solved very largely this problem of the person dying from cancer of the bowel. It is generally agreed, even by those who support euthanasia, that there are institutions, manned by doctors and nurses who cater specially for this problem, and in them patients spend their terminal illness with almost no pain and distress. The question then emerges whether these institutions should not be multiplied and more training be given to doctors and nurses in these aspects of the care of terminal illness. One also has to ask why this has not occurred. These are all points to be discussed in the final chapter.

One would also like to know in the case of the man dying with cancer of the bowel, whether he knew he had cancer and also knew that he was dying. Did Williams discuss this point with his friend? Evidence will be produced in this chapter to show that relatives and friends seldom discuss either cancer or death with a patient. Unless this is done it is almost impossible to discuss voluntary euthanasia. Or did the desire for death arise largely or entirely in the understandable agony of the visitor? Again was the patient, heavily drugged with morphine and leading an 'artificial twilight existence' in a position to make a legally valid request for euthanasia? Would suicide have met the occasion, and, if legally permissible, would the visitor have administered the tablets and sat by to obstruct any attempt at resuscitation? Should it cease to be an offence to abet suicide under circumstances such as these?

These questions however are too agonizing to be dismissed by legal quibbles or medical niceties, even if this illustrates different facets of the problem. My own father, years after it occurred, always broke down when he described his own father's death from cancer of the rectum early in the present century. I always gathered that there were no morphine injections, you just took some tablets by mouth and went on moaning. The problem has decreased but it is certainly still with us. In 1959 a doctor interviewed the relatives of those dying at home of cancer and he obtained vivid descriptions of pain in 20% of cases.[2] A more recent survey in 1965 of cancer patients dying at home found that among 400 patients some 8% had severe difficulties in obtaining relief from pain.[3] In certain institutions for the relief of severe pain in patients dying of cancer it is stated that severe pain unrelieved by the appropriate treatment hardly ever occurs.[4]

The dead give no evidence. Relatives and friends do. It is important to assess their evidence, especially as it is only in recent years that there has been any study of the emotions that arise in bereavement. Much depends on the closeness of the relationship between the bereaved and the one who died. If very close, as between spouses, or between parents and child, at first the bereaved person is numb, being dazed with grief, hardly able to accept the reality of the loss. Deep waves of grief burst over the person from time to time, often lasting for some fifteen to thirty minutes. These are natural, and if they are unreasonably suppressed serious mental illness may follow. Slowly these waves of grief subside, but they come to be dreaded. Loss of sleep, of appetite and of weight occurs. These are the manifestations of grief; they must be worked through for a period of time that varies from a few weeks to two years, even longer.[5] Many spouses never recover completely although they may preserve an outward calm and are even praised for their serenity. Much depends on the depth of the relationship established beforehand with the deceased. It may be intense for a spouse; parental grief is said to be often life-long if a child has grown to become a young adult and dies suddenly, of an accident or even in war. On the other hand, when an aged person dies, this is regarded as natural. The mourning has been worked through even before death occurs and there may be little sense of bereavement.

The depth and the duration of the grief are always more severe if the loss was sudden and untimely.[6] It is especially severe after suicide, for the bereaved often feel that they proved inadequate.[7] They blame themselves and feel guilty.[8] On the other hand, if there has been a long illness with a progressive incurable complaint, then death may cause no distress; it is often a relief. Probably death is regarded as a natural release from pain and disability. The work of mourning, the sense of loss, took place before the death occurred.

Other more complex feelings are apt to mark the period of mourning, especially if the grief is severe and the patient suffered excessively. Guilt is often felt. The relative often feels that he has contributed to the person's death by not insisting on early medical treatment; perhaps he aggravated the illness by encouraging work and activity. Unexplained hostility also often arises; it is displaced and vented on the clergyman as the representative of God who brought untimely death or on the doctor who failed as the guardian of life.[9] Rehearsing in memory the events which led up to fatal illness and the distressing scenes that perhaps characterized the terminal stage, the relative may prove an unreliable witness about the extent of the death agony. He may exaggerate, even prevaricate, quite unintentionally. It is therefore difficult to evaluate the stories told by bereaved relatives concerning the amount of suffering experienced by the patients. They may prove quite unreliable witnesses concerning whether the patient expressed a determined, informed and rational wish for death. The distress of the relatives may be projected into the mumbled incoherent remarks of someone drugged and dying. All this must not be construed as an attempt on the part of the author to belittle the grief of the relatives or the fact that certain patients die with pain only partially relieved. It must be recognized however that guilt and hostility colour all memories of death. It must also be recognized that feelings of guilt and hostility would also colour the memory and judgment of many relatives, if they were ever called upon to agree to voluntary euthanasia in someone dearly loved. As the next section goes on to discuss, there is often a complete breakdown of communication in depth between relatives and the patient, an iron curtain of concealment has descended between them.

If voluntary euthanasia were administered, it is probable that pathological reactions of grief would occur if the death resembled suicide; that is to say if the patient received it early in his illness, while still fairly fit, and before the relatives had become accustomed to the idea of an inevitable, impending loss. Reaction would be severe if euthanasia was administered without the knowledge of the relatives, or against their objections, since this would appear akin to suicide; it might suggest murder to anyone emotionally distraught. Suicide might suggest cowardice, it would suggest rejection.

If, on the other hand, voluntary euthanasia were administered to someone who had been ill for a long period of time with a progressive incurable illness, characterized by much unrelieved distress, there might be a few regrets by the relatives; there might even be a strong sense of relief, even a sense of thankfulness. This would occur more easily if the patient had achieved a normal span of life and he had expressed a steady determination to die.

To tell or not to tell

It is axiomatic that voluntary euthanasia would require the active co-operation of the medical profession in two respects. First, a fair proportion of doctors would have to be prepared to administer euthanasia[10] – a point discussed later. Secondly all doctors would have to be prepared to inform a patient who has a painful, incurable complaint concerning his plight so that he can make a choice.[11] This, it was stated by advocates of voluntary euthanasia, should occur early in the disease, so that, if desired, the patient could avoid a long period of suffering. Another reason in favour of an early decision in a painful, incurable, progressive illness, such as cancer, would be to obviate the difficulties of decision during the terminal stages of the complaint. Those who support voluntary euthanasia admit that often there can be no rational discussion at that stage of the issues involved.[12] It is therefore advocated that healthy adults in the prime of life should sign and subsequently confirm an advance declaration. Unless this is revoked it could be executed without delay as soon as the patient had been informed by his own doctor and by a consultant that an incurable, distressing complaint had been diagnosed.

The difficulties in informing the patient that he has an incurable, progressive, painful disease are exemplified in the case of cancer. If the disease has spread widely throughout the body, and surgery, radiology and other forms of treatment have been tried, a stage may be reached at which no further curative measures are contemplated, although much can be done to ease pain and relieve distress. Then the question emerges and is usually stated, somewhat crudely, thus: Should a doctor tell? This however is not a simple question. It is not even a single question. It assumes that there is a single simple truth and that the doctor knows it. In actual fact the doctor has formed an opinion that cancer is indeed present, but there are many varieties of cancer. I myself have had a few rodent ulcers removed at a series of operations; this is a form of cancer, but it almost never recurs. The doctor must grasp the truth as he understands it and translate it into language that the patient can understand. This concerns both the diagnosis – what disease is present – but also the prognosis – the probable outcome of the disease in this particular patient. The doctor has only a partial insight into 'the truth', and all communication is difficult. Misunderstandings may arise.

Patients vary, not only in their resistance to every disease, including cancer, but also in their conscious and unconscious mental reactions. What the patient wishes to know varies; some wish to know the whole truth, however unpalatable, others say that they wish to know the truth, but only if it is hopeful! The majority of people in Britain, when in health, state that they wish to be told the diagnosis of cancer should they develop this disease, but it is possible that not so many would continue to affirm their desire if they actually contracted a malignant illness.

The 'truth' about any disease varies from time to time during the development of the disease. During the initial stages of cancer the surgeon may be able to reassure the patient with absolute truthfulness. Probably the news is whispered briefly to the patient while he is recovering from the operation that the mass was small, the disease caught at an early stage, that there were no signs of spread to other parts of the body, that there is every prospect that all the malignant disease has been removed and that it is hoped that there will never be any recurrence. Should these occur many years later there is still hope that they will be few in number and that they too can be eradicated. In certain cases radiotherapy too will decrease the risk of any return of the disease; chemotherapy may play an important part. When a patient convalescent from an operation for a malignant mass can truthfully be told all this, then is truth mingled with hope. It has been well said that hope should die only a short time before the patient.

Perhaps years later – the length often varies – in a certain proportion of patients recurrences occur. Some can be dealt with, others cannot. With the latter group then the question to tell or not to tell becomes more painful and more pressing; perhaps we are approaching the closing scenes of the play called life. None of the actors are new; all of them have compromised themselves in the thrust and counterthrust by which we come to terms with the truth. Both patient and doctor have offered hostages to fortune. Perhaps the doctor, moved by sympathy with the patient, has encouraged optimism and overplayed hopefulness. Probably he has dabbled in understatement, even compromised himself by prevarication. He has played for time, a more favourable time; he has procrastinated so long that a little longer seems neither here nor there.

The patient too has his part to play in these final scenes. Although the principal actor, he has no knowledge about how it will end. He has put out feelers towards the doctor on several occasions, only to be met with half-truths and double-talk. He too has learned to wear a mask to conceal his fears. Gazing into the mirror of truth he has come to deceive himself. He senses vaguely that he is the centre of a conspiracy of silence. He too has found his path through the changing scenes of his illness; fears and phantasies have lurked in the secret sessions of night-time wakefulness; hope has lightened many a grey dawn. The day arrives and the patient must don his mask once more.

Almost invariably the relatives are admitted to the dread secret. They turn up in unexpectedly large numbers as the play develops, but having taken the oath of secrecy, they are admitted immediately to the stage on which the principal actor lies, apparently innocent of his fate. They are not all good actors; they keep 'off the subject', some with false jollity, others adopt an offhand matter. Many find that they cannot cope with this duplicity for long; hurriedly they make their excuses and depart. All this provides many clues to a fearful patient.

The strain on a spouse, sworn to secrecy, can be tremendous. It has been condemned by those who have observed the situation in any detail, notably sociologists[13] and psychiatrists[14] who interview those who are dying or those who are bereaved. It has seldom been condemned in plain language by doctors. Eminent physicians have stated that the question whether to tell a patient he is dying from cancer, or any other disease, seems to arise but seldom.[15] Lord Platt, a President of the Royal College of Physicians, summed up well the reason why the question to tell or not to tell seldom arises: it has been strangled in the conspiracy of silence:

Lay people are naturally interested to know a doctor's view on what he should tell his patients; but in fact the question does not arise as often as they think. For a conspiracy of silence usually surrounds the whole question of death, a silence as much due to the patient's avoidance of the subject as the doctor's.[16]

As will be discussed shortly, there is abundant evidence from physicians, psychiatrists and sociologists who have encouraged the dying to speak freely, that the large majority who have an alert mind fear death, they know that they are dying and many wish to talk about it. The most outstanding criticism of this conspiracy of silence which surrounds the terminal stages of cancer, and indeed many deathbeds, came from a doctor, himself dying of Hodgkin's disease (a form of cancer) while he wrote it.[17] He described the pathetic charade that surrounds this deathbed, with so much unhappiness, depression and loneliness. It is not edifying to so many relatives to see the doctor deliberately deceiving a patient: one day a relative may himself become a patient.

There is also the question of how to tell the truth. It can only be done by someone who has established a position of trust and sympathy with the patient. Ultimately it is the responsibility of the doctor who is in charge of the patient; in hospital this is the consultant, at home it is the general medical practitioner. They may at times delegate their responsibility to a nursing sister or a chaplain, or someone else. They may decide that it is best done by the spouse or nearest friend. Even when someone else undertakes the task, the spouse or close friend should be present and be prepared to stay for a very long period of time with the patient who has received news of his departure. Patients will need to be reassured that they will not be expected to suffer severe pain; analgesic and narcotic drugs will look after that.

They must still be given hope. Everything possible will be done; new investigations, new treatments will be attempted, new sedatives used.

In actual practice the matter seldom goes quite like this. Possibly the patient works out the diagnosis, the significance of the big operation, the need for radiotherapy. Often there is procrastination, probing questions of the patient are deflected; people play for time, hoping that they will never have to face this most difficult moment: the moment of truth, which is the sentence of death. But if many people surround the patient and know the dread diagnosis, sooner or later most patients realize the true state of affairs. Few people can wear a mask for long, they whisper or their voices assume an unaccustomed tone, words catch in the throat, and eyes moisten. They blow the nose and conceal the face with a handkerchief. They are not themselves. Then the patient, too, learns to wear a mask, sometimes an impenetrable mask; but out of two hundred patients suffering from terminal illness, mostly cancer, one psychiatrist who learned to listen considered all but three knew they were dying,[18] and almost all who had cancer knew about the diagnosis even if they could not discuss it openly with friends and relatives, nurses and doctors.

How to tell the cancer patient

Those who have most experience of this problem of letting a patient know that he has cancer, perhaps even that there is not long to live, insist that the question for the doctor is never 'To tell or not to tell'. Cicely Saunders, from her great experience at St Joseph's and St Christopher's Hospices, to which many patients go in the terminal stages of cancer, says that the question is always 'What do you let your patients tell you?'[19] It consists in listening to a patient, evaluating all the clues, providing the right personal relationship within which defences lower and fears come out into the open. Elizabeth Kübler-Ross[20] from her great experience among cancer patients dying in the Billings Hospital, Chicago, insists that the question should be re-worded as 'How do I share this with my patient?' Both of these doctors agree that there can be no general rules; patients vary enormously as individuals. The approach must be on an individual basis, with sympathy and always with some grounds, however small, for hope. It is interesting, and possibly not an accident, that both of these authorities are women. Dr Cicely Saunders qualified as a nurse, a social worker and a doctor and has worked exclusively with this problem. Dr Elizabeth Kübler-Ross is a doctor and psychiatrist in the Department of Psychiatry at the University of Chicago.

Meanwhile how does the question resolve itself among the rough and tumble of general medical practice, the care of people dying at home, or in the busy hospital wards? Professor Cramond summarized the position recently by saying that 80% of dying patients know that they are dying and would wish to talk about it, and that 80% of doctors deny this and believe that the patient should never be told.[21] A most cruel paradox, but true.

Recently 1,250 general medical practitioners in Britain answered an extensive questionnaire on terminal illness.[22] In general terms it can be stated that these doctors stated that they always told the relatives but they rarely told the patient who was dying. More precisely, 95% said that they nearly always told the relatives that the man was dying, but half of these (48% of the survey) went on to say that they never told any patient, while 42% said they told rather under a quarter of their patients.

An earlier survey in the United Kingdom in 1960[23] summarized views obtained in some three hundred hospitals and homes for terminal care. It reported that on the whole the feeling was that normally the truth should be withheld, but that the relatives were usually told and that they found it very difficult to keep up the deception. Confidence could be lost if a patient was deceived, but at the same time it was wrong to tell him. It was noted that many patients practised self-deception; they could also deceive others. The staff frankly admitted deliberate deception; even when they knew the answer was death or cancer, they would say 'I don't know'. This report was perceptive in noting that patients seldom ask 'Am I going to die?', but that the question is framed the other way 'Am I going to get better?'

Very solidly over the years the great weight of medical tradition, both in doctors and nurses, has been that it is remarkable how few patients make a specific request for information about the possibility of death. The older clinical teachers in Britain taught that most dying persons refused to face any question of their own decease.[24] It is only in recent years has there been any recognition of the patient's rights in this respect. Several enquiries by psychiatrists and social workers have confirmed the lamentable state of affairs which may result when there is a failure of communication between doctor and patient when cancer has been detected, especially if it has already spread to other

parts of the body and is inoperable. True, not everyone can take the
news of his decease calmly, but others are sufficiently mature to do so.
Such a one was the late Professor J. B. S. Haldane. I attended a conference at the Ciba Foundation at which he gave a brilliant concluding paper, one worthy of the symposium on *Man and His Future*. I
remember hearing that he had to see a surgeon at the end of the
conference, but I did not realize, ironically, that it was about his personal future. After his death his sister wrote a scathing letter to the
British Medical Journal:

Sooner or later many families are faced with the alarming and disquiet-
ing question: Has the operating surgeon told the facts about the operation,
either to the patient or to his nearest relatives? This is at present entirely a
matter for the surgeon's judgment. I submit that there should be a policy
laid down which would encourage the surgeon to tell intelligent and well-
balanced patients whether, for example, their probable chances of life
should be estimated in months or years. My brother, Professor Haldane,
has recently died of a secondary cancer. When he left hospital he was under
the impression that he had at least another two or three years in which to
initiate and complete various pieces of scientific work, deal with the affairs
of his institute etc. The lives and plans of a number of other people were
involved; some of them feel bitterly about this. The surgeon writes that
though he made it perfectly clear to both my brother and his wife that he
was available during my brother's convalescence to discuss his future, they
never broached the matter. In fact, his wife left England (for India) two or
three months before my brother himself did, clearly thinking that the
operation had been successful. The operation, certainly, had been successful; what she did not know was that cancer had spread to the liver. Now I
am sure that the surgeon behaved absolutely correctly. But I must add that
before my brother went into hospital it was particularly brought to the
notice of the hospital authorities that he was the kind of person who ought
to be told what was happening to him. Several responsible people tried to
find out, but the pattern of medical hierarchy prevented this. I would have
supposed that there might have been some positive public duty on the part
of the hospital or the surgeon to warn my brother, who had often faced
death before. The time was bound to come when he felt he had been cheated
and treated like a child . . . A new code is required.[25]

It is impossible to defend this failure of communication. Unfortunately in my experience it is all too common. Quite often it resolves
itself into a game of mutual bluff: the surgeon feels himself under an
obligation to say nothing, or as little as possible and the patient feels
that he will not take the initiative. 'If there is bad news,' he argues,
'surely they will tell me.' On the other hand psychiatrists and sociologists who have looked into this problem state that if the bad news
is told too abruptly and without sympathy, it can create a terrible

scene. I shall always remember the hush that came over the out-patient surgical clinic at St Thomas's Hospital in the mid-1920s. A patient had an ulcer on his tongue; we all looked at it, some touched it. He asked, 'Is it cancer?' 'Yes' said the surgeon; no more and yet no less. There was silence among the medical students for what seemed an eternity. So many surgeons believe rightly or wrongly that one should never, never tell a patient that he has cancer. It is like a death sentence. Yet no one likes telling a lie; but lies are told, even in my experience when mature people in middle age have insisted on the truth. Often the spouse, or the nearest of kin is told. While not agree-ing with those who say that a doctor straight away should inform every adult if he has cancer, I wish to record that I was a clergyman in three separate parishes in England during a space of ten years and in every case that this occurred to a parishioner; the patient came to know the truth in the end, but could not confess this fact to the spouse, who thought that the secret had been kept, and believed the other did not know. In utter loneliness of spirit each said silently, 'I know about it; you don't know about it, but I can maintain the lie that lasts until death do us part.'

A sociologist quoted a typical statement of a middle-aged widow.

I knew he was dying, but he didn't. It didn't sink in, the doctor told me . . . It was terrible having to lie to him; I had to be cruel really. I was abrupt with him sort of, or I would have broke down.

And again from another widow:

He was ill for twenty-two months with cancer. I knew, but he didn't . . . It was a great strain; I'd break down when he was upstairs . . . My doctor said *he* wasn't going to tell him and the hospital wouldn't either; so if I tell him, he's not going to have much faith in the hospital, is he? It's just one of those things. I told him awful lies.[26]

In the United States patients appear to be more sophisticated than in Britain. The means of communication, television, newspapers, magazines and books have alerted them to the significance of disease. American patients are conscious of the fact that they pay for the ser-vices of their doctors. They expect to be told the diagnosis and the prognosis. It is recognized by the medical profession that the patient has a legal right to know the diagnosis. It belongs to him; it is his property; he has paid for it. It could be an offence to conceal the nature of the complaint; legal action could be taken if deceit occur-red.[27] Americans may have medical check-ups at regular intervals.

They expect to hear about any illnesses detected. They anticipate that directions will be given about diet, and that explanations will be offered about the treatment of any defects discovered at the medical check-up. There is less reticence about disease in the United States. Newspapers and television report details concerning the ailments of public figures, such as the last illnesses of General Eisenhower. The American public has become well informed about psycho-analysis, and there are counsellors for all the crises of life. No subject is taboo and it is symptomatic of that great country that there have appeared in recent years two scientific journals on death, the *Journal of Thanatology* and *Omega*. There is even an Institute of Thanatology, which endeavours to study all aspects of the subject of death.

Americans who fall victim to cancer are probably better informed about it than are their opposite numbers in Britain. The healthy members of the American public insist almost to a man that they would wish to hear about the diagnosis if they ever developed malignant disease; one investigation put the proportion as 98·5% of adults,[28] and other surveys support this high figure.[29] (In Edinburgh the comparable figure for healthy adults was assessed at about two-thirds of the population.)[30] When however in America patients who were actually suffering from cancer were asked the same question the figure had dropped to 89%. American doctors appear to be more willing than their British colleagues to inform a patient that he has cancer. Thus among 1,300 United States doctors some 57% agreed that this was their standard practice.[31]

However, when one reads the American literature on cancer patients admitted to hospitals for terminal care, one gets the impression that even in that country there is still a very large proportion of whom the staff would say that they have never been told the facts, even if they have all too often worked out the answer for themselves.[32]

Cancer patients' reactions to being told

It is possible to study the reaction of patients to their awareness that they have cancer. This is possibly one of the last areas of life to be explored by the dynamically minded psychiatrists. It is this type of person, the man who has come to realize that he has cancer, who might choose voluntary euthanasia if it was legalized. There have been few studies of these patients that reflect psycho-analytic insights. A detailed account of a young married woman dying of widespread metastases of breast cancer was published in 1963, and in 1970 Professor W. A. Cramond described his observations on the psychotherapy of patients dying of cancer. He offered short notes to illustrate the main points of his paper and brief notes on four patients dying from cancer and one patient dying from leukaemia.[33] General articles also occur, but original work employing detailed observations is meagre in the extreme.

Recently a book has been published with much original data, records of the tape-recorded interviews of two hundred American patients dying mostly of cancer. The work is that of Dr Elizabeth Kübler-Ross, of the Department of Psychiatry at the University of Chicago, at Billings Hospital. As a serious scientific investigation the matter started in an unusual manner. In 1965 Dr Kübler-Ross was approached by four theology students of the Chicago Theological Seminary about research into death as the biggest crisis in human life. Instead of reading the existing medical and psychiatric literature on the subject, they took the novel line that they would ask the dying patients to be their teachers. They encountered enormous difficulties and much opposition from the medical and nursing staff in obtaining access to terminally ill patients. Eventually they succeeded and once a week over a period of two years one or two patients were interviewed in a private room of the hospital. After telling the patient that the team were endeavouring to obtain information concerning patients who were very sick, or even dying, permission was sought, and obtained, to tape-record the interview. At the start it took an average of ten hours a week to get permission from reluctant doctors to obtain a single patient to be interviewed; by the end of the research project this opposition had largely disappeared. At the weekly seminars sophisticated techniques ensured apparent privacy to the patient, but the proceedings could be watched and heard by the concealed audience of as many as fifty people from all the helping professions, doctors, psychiatrists, nurses, social workers, clergymen and rabbis.

Less than 2% of the patients invited to participate in the seminar refused. All patients were asked how they came to know about the nature of their complaint, and an attempt was made to assess if they knew they had entered the terminal stage of their illness. Many lived only a few hours or days after the interview; some survived for a few months. Out of the two hundred patients only three attempted to deny the approach of death unto the very end of life.[34] Many were dying from cancer and almost all of these knew that they had malignant disease, even when the staff and the relatives were certain that they did not.[35] Patients had worked this out mostly from clues supplied by the nature of their treatment, the significance of an operation, or the radiotherapy; others had been alerted by the peculiar behaviour of relatives who were privy to the diagnosis; a minority had been informed directly by their doctors.

Patients were specifically asked whether they had been informed in an acceptable manner; they were encouraged to talk about the evasions of doctors and of relatives. Two points appeared to emerge. First, it was the attitude of the doctors, nurses and relatives to dying and to death which determined whether patients could approach them with their fears of cancer and their dread of death. Only those members of the staff who had confronted death in their own minds could help patients to know that they had cancer or that they were dying. Those people, be it doctor or nurse or relative, to whom death was a frightening, horrible taboo subject could not discuss the matter with the patient. If it was the doctor who adopted this point of view, then he defended himself quite unconsciously by saying that patients did not want to know the truth and that they never asked about it. To him all was well; he was not conscious that it was his own attitude which provoked this reaction.

There were two things on which patients needed help from doctors, nurses and relatives: one was dying, its pains and distresses, but the other was death itself, the state of not-being, at least in any earthly sense.[36] The diagnosis of cancer was particularly feared by all concerned; it was synonymous with a painful and protracted dying and also with death and not-being. One had to minister to both with reassurance and hope.

The second fact that emerged was that patients reacted to the knowledge of terminal illness or cancer in a variety of different ways according to certain psychological characteristics, compounded of past experiences and customary patterns of defence.[37] Those who had learned to solve life's problems faced cancer, dying and death; those who had reacted to life's problems by denial and evasion would deny cancer or its implications for a long period of time. It was dangerous for a patient to be informed of cancer and of death prematurely or too abruptly, especially by someone with whom he had not established a relationship of warmth and trust.

Patients faced with the certainty of cancer, or any progressive disease, were at first in a state of mental shock; they usually reacted at first by denial. They could not realize it was indeed they who had the disease. Partial denial was employed by almost all patients, not only at the first confrontation, but also later on from time to time; in a very few right up to death itself. Denial however was usually only a temporary affair and gave way to periods of acceptance. Then they talked briefly about the real situation, but suddenly indicated their inability to look at it realistically so they changed the conversation.[38] A patient might acknowledge it at times, at other times deny it, especially to members of the hospital staff or relatives who could not bear the topic.[39] This is the main reason for the great discrepancy of opinion about whether patients wish to know about cancer and death. Patients without a sound religious background may take weeks or months before they can accept death without becoming psychotic or suicidal.[40]

Denial was usually followed by anger, rage and resentment. Patients became critical of the hospital, doctors and nurses that had failed to cure them and of the God who had not answered their prayers. They became querulous, demanding little attentions, envious of those who remained healthy. Relationships within the family often became strained as anger, ingratitude and resentment obtruded on many occasions. Anger was sometimes followed by bargaining, at least among those who had a religious faith, and it was surprising how many had some remnant of belief hidden away in the depths. Patients tended to bargain with God, that if they got better, so and so would happen; and evidence of guilt came peeping out.

All this gave way to depression, the longest and most outstanding feature of all terminally ill cancer persons. This however is but right and natural; it is preparatory to the ultimate separation. Like the mourning of relatives after the death of their loved one, this grief, too, is a necessary step; it paves the way to ultimate acceptance of death. Reassurances, encouragements, even medical treatment for depression, as if it were like another psychiatric illness, are to be deprecated. All the classical signs of depression are there: the apathy, poor appetite, poor sleep, constipation, and desire for isolation and even a desire for death.[41]

Depression however gave way at last to quiet acceptance. No longer was the patient angry or depressed with his fate. Tiredness and weakness increased, he dozed off frequently. Feeling had drained away, conversation was short, interests contracted. Communication was often largely non-verbal, the look of the eyes, the grasp of the hand. The struggle was over. There is always peace at the last, always.

At all stages, even to the very end, there were strands of hope. Then again the stages did not fall into rigid categories, anger and even denial interspersed long periods of depression. Hope was not at times unrewarded; approximately half of the group investigated, all of whom were considered to have a terminal illness, most of them having cancer, recovered sufficiently to go home for a period of time, being readmitted later to die in the same hospital.[42] These periods of remission were much valued. At all stages it was essential to preserve some measure of hope; hope that the condition would improve to allow a period at home, hope of new treatments to be tried, of new drugs, even of new discoveries, even new miracles. Patients were always hoping to find some meaning in life, even in their periods of weakness, pain and depression.[43] The period of acceptance was usually short, a matter of a few days or hours.

These observations of Dr Kübler-Ross do not stand alone, although they are some of the fullest records of dying persons, the recorded interviews being conducted by a psychiatrist, but many of the questions were put by the doctor, chaplain or even a student. The lengthy records have the freshness of real life.

There was almost no attempt to correlate these findings with that of previous workers in this field. There has been much investigation in the USA of the psychological aspects of patients who know that they are suffering from cancer. There is widespread agreement about denial.[44] Denial helps the patient to cope with the situation; it also helps the doctors to avoid discussions with the patient.[45] Probably all patients with malignant disease have some awareness of the fact,[46] but there are various levels of awareness, which also fluctuate from time to time.[47]

The second widely recognized fact that emerges from all these investigations of cancer is depression. Psychiatrists who have spent literally thousands of hours analysing cancer patients have written of their despair, one deeper even than that of psychiatric patients who suffer from a psychosis of depression.[48]

In concluding this section on the psychological reactions of cancer patients it must be asked: what would voluntary euthanasia offer? It would certainly shorten the very real agony of the relatives, but it would often increase their natural sense of guilt in bereavement. It would provide a deep embarrassment for the doctors, most of whom in all countries and cultures find it extremely painful to discuss openly at least at an early stage, this dread diagnosis.

Would voluntary euthanasia aid the cancer patient, seen by psychiatrists, doctors, nurses and relatives as set against a kaleido-scopic background of levels of awareness, coupled with long periods of denial, rumblings of anger, clouds of despair, yet interspersed with periods of hope? The only steady state is that of the final serene and sedated acceptance of death. Voluntary euthanasia demands a rational, steady, determined, informed desire for death. This is usually impossible in the changing moods and denials of the terminal stages of cancer.

Can the bleak depression of terminal cancer be distinguished by a psychiatrist from a totally different state, the primary psychiatric ill-ness called depression? The psychiatric illness of depression may arise from a physical disease, such as a deficiency of thyroid secretion; cure can then be effected by the appropriate hormone therapy. Depression usually arises as a psychiatric illness, without associated physical causes, such as a disease of the thyroid gland or cancer. The psychia-tric disease of depression can often be cured completely by modern treatment, then the desire for death passes. All forms of depression lead to a desire for death and the commonest cause of suicide is depression. It would be difficult, if not impossible, to know whether the desire for voluntary euthanasia in a cancer patient was the valid decision of a sane man, or the morbid desire of a depressed psychiatric state.

Quite apart from depression, it is also a fact that the cancer patient in the terminal stage may be habituated to narcotic drugs and stuporose from sedative drugs. All this would make it difficult, if not impossible, for him to make a valid decision about euthanasia. Having registered his decision would not the mood change, hope reappear or denial reassert itself? In many hospitals and most homes, with the prevailing conspiracy of silence, where death is a taboo sub-ject, how could the patient, relatives or doctor begin to discuss in a meaningful way the idea of choosing death by voluntary euthanasia? It should also be borne in mind that half the patients interviewed by Dr Kübler-Ross in a Chicago hospital because they had a terminal illness, usually cancer, improved sufficiently to return home or to a nursing home and appeared grateful for this period, however brief, of improved health. Even in London, out of the carefully selected cancer patients who had been admitted to die in a special institution, Dr

Cicely Saunders reported that a proportion by no means small were discharged to their homes for a period of improved health. When the author visited the hospital recently on a bank holiday Monday only sixteen out of the fifty-four terminal patients had chosen to stay in bed; all the others were either in the garden or at home. This is good terminal care among a group of patients, most of whom had severe pain in the last stages of cancer.

Progressive chronic diseases

The question whether to tell, what to tell, and when to tell occurs most acutely in any person who has cancer, but the same problem arises in other fatal diseases. Those psychiatrists who have observed patients coming to terms with their own mortality, see no fundamental difference between the reactions of patients who have cancer and of those who have other progressive fatal diseases.[49] Probably in other diseases, hope plays a larger part in the early reactions to the illness, but eventually the psychological processes by which a person comes to accept death appear largely identical: denial, anger, depression and finally acceptance. Hope remains a prominent feature most of the time until the very end, that is, the terminal stage.

Perhaps it should be repeated that people react to the phases of their illnesses in different ways according to their temperament and past experience. Those who have gone through life evading issues, finding escape in forgetfulness and phantasy, react to illness in the same manner by means of prolonged denial. The bellicose person vents his anger on the circumstances that in his opinion led to the illness, or he can rail against the inefficiency of the doctors. Even Job was exhorted by his wife to curse God and die.[50] Depression appears but natural in any chronic progressive disease; it may deepen into an actual psychosis; it may end in suicide.

There are numerous chronic diseases of most of the organs of the body, many of which are seldom completely cured. Some of these tend to be progressive, but in an erratic manner, such as occurs in multiple sclerosis, a common form of paralysis starting in adult life. Other diseases occur in short severe episodes, but tend to recur. Thus a man may get more than one attack of coronary thrombosis; in between he may be quite fit but sooner or later one attack may prove too much for him. Quite a number however never get a second attack; they feel cured, and are cured. On the other hand one or more attacks may lead to chronic heart failure, which tends to be slowly progressive. High blood pressure is another condition which many people have to a mild degree, but in some this tends to be a progressive disability, unless continuous treatment keeps it in control. Diabetes, when once established, tends to remain as a chronic disorder; fortunately it can be well controlled by treatment nowadays, but complications, which can be very serious, may occur. Many other diseases can lead to progressive failure of the heart, liver, kidneys or even lungs. Thus attacks of bronchitis may become severe and chronic, especially in those who smoke cigarettes, and then the condition tends to be chronic and progressive. On the other hand, most people who get bronchitis never develop into a chronic, incurable state; they get an attack or so every winter, but are quite well every summer. Although never fatal, chronic disease of the bones, as in Paget's disease (common in elderly people), tends to be slowly progressive.

Certain varieties of arthritis, such as rheumatoid arthritis, can cause much pain for many years. More than one physician has stated that in his opinion a few of those who suffer from rheumatoid arthritis have more pain than occurs in cancer. The arthritic person lives with his disability and pain for many years, five to twenty years perhaps, but the patient who has painful malignant disease can reckon on usually only a few months of pain, should this ever occur, because death brings release, and he can be given narcotic drugs in a liberal manner. In fact there are a whole number of non-fatal complaints which can be characterized by great pain. Neuralgia of the face, especially the so-called trigeminal variety, or that which follows a virus infection of herpes, may give bouts of excruciating pain. Quite a number of chronic diseases of the nervous system can be very painful, especially if the sensory nerves are involved.

All diseases which are characterized by great pain may be extremely difficult to treat, unless the problem in a sense solves itself by death in a few months. Narcotic drugs, such as morphine, always cause tolerance and even addiction if continued for many months; they may be given to someone who has widespread cancer, who has only a few weeks or months of life, but they should never be given for many days to anyone who has a non-fatal painful disorder. Many modern analgesic drugs may be tried and can give great relief in persons who have chronic pain, but it is still true that some patients having, say, trigeminal neuralgia, rheumatoid arthritis or angina may have a good deal of pain, only partially relieved, intermittently for some years.

Certain other chronic diseases may not threaten life, they may cause little pain, but they can cause much distress, frustration and disability. Anyone having one of these disorders must be tempted to ask himself at times whether life is worth living. Stone in the kidney or bladder, likewise stone in the gall-bladder, used to cause years of severe attacks of colic, but nowadays modern surgery can usually remove the stone. Those who have suffocating attacks, in which they fight for their breath, are some of the most pitiful of all patients. It is a very terrible thing to feel that one cannot get one's breath; a fearful dread possesses one. Some persons who have chronic bronchitis and emphysema have these attacks of suffocated difficult breathing, called dyspnoea. Asthma, if severe, can be very frightening, even if seldom threatening to life; so can the forced laboured breathing found in certain varieties of heart failure.

Certain forms of neurological disease, although causing strictly speaking no pain, can cause slow progressive paralysis, so that the person first of all cannot walk, or use his arms, then he takes to his bed. These long-term neurological complaints, although uncommon, are a great burden to the victims themselves and to the nursing staff who do everything for them. More than one such person must have wondered at times whether life was worth living. At the other end of the scale there are certain skin disorders which can be extremely distressing and disfiguring. Because of this dermatological disorder a man may lose his employment; some of these diseases are extremely chronic in duration; some are incurable. The skin may itch most of the time until a man is almost crazy with scratching, there may be offensive discharging sore areas, or large areas of the skin may be covered by ointment, pastes or lotions. Sufferers can never forget their skin, which prickles, tickles, itches or smarts much of the time. Sleeping is disturbed and profound mental changes may occur.

All of these complaints, those which have just been mentioned and many others, could have qualified for an application for voluntary euthanasia under the Voluntary Euthanasia Bill (1969). Some of these diseases will never threaten life, but others may in a certain proportion of cases. In these chronic disorders a doctor usually finds no difficulty in telling the patient what disease is present; in fact the patient demands to know the general category of disorder that has taken him to the doctor or hospital. He expects to hear if it is a coronary attack, or rheumatoid arthritis, or diabetes, or high blood pressure. Fortunately none of these words have the dread overtones of the term cancer.

In these chronic disorders the real difficulty concerns any discussion of the prognosis. How long am I going to be ill? What can be done for me? Will I get rid of this illness? These are natural questions on the lips of any patient. Here one strikes a fundamental difficulty: if the patient can be inspired with hope his chances of getting better are much improved. He will co-operate with treatment and the whole atmosphere of hope undoubtedly exerts a beneficial effect on almost all complaints. A hopeful man feels he is getting better and in many cases objective assessment employing accurate scientific measurements demonstrates that he is in very truth improving. Thus, to give one example, if after a certain variety of heart attack a patient has a fifty-fifty chance of making a full recovery, and this patient believes he will be in the lucky half, his chances now are distinctly better.

His chances would be considerably reduced if he was to hear that many people die from his disorder, or that many make a poor recovery, or even that some people have 'qualified' for voluntary euthanasia with his complaint. If legislation on voluntary euthanasia were ever enacted, it appears certain, whatever its supporters say, that publicity would soon be alerted concerning which disorders 'qualified' for administration of voluntary euthanasia to those applying for it. Cancer and leukaemia would be early known competitors, but then soon it would be realized that euthanasia was being administered, if requested, in those making a poor recovery from a stroke. It would be known that euthanasia could be administered upon request if there were poor recovery from a coronary attack, and this knowledge would be remembered in the night watches by those new patients who watch the machines that monitor their heart beats. They too, would see the writing on the wall. Slowly it would be realized that some patients with poor recovery from ulcerative colitis had asked for and received euthanasia. Then ulcerative colitis will be 'on the list', and the many thousands who suffer from this complaint on-and-off for several years will feel their bowels move within them. Those house-bound and chair-bound from arthritis will hear on the radio that someone with their complaint 'has qualified' in an application. When the local club for the physically handicapped meets it will prove a useful talking point to whisper that multiple sclerosis apparently easily qualifies; certain doctors regard applications most favourably. Those attending the diabetic clinic in a hospital outpatient department, having all of them an 'irremediable condition' under the terms of the Voluntary Euthanasia Bill (1969), will learn eventually that certain of the senior members of their club have qualified for application, because 'complications' due to diabetes occurred. Before, these diabetics had not realized that the complications of diabetes might be fatal, but under the new and merciful regime of voluntary euthanasia, the commonest fatality of all would be hope.

VI

The Principle of Voluntary Euthanasia

There are four long essays written in recent years on the principle of voluntary euthanasia, one by Professor Glanville Williams (1958) Rouse Ball Professor of the Laws of England at Cambridge,[1] a second by Professor Antony Flew (1969) Professor of Philosophy at Keele University on 'The Principle of Euthanasia',[2] and two essays by Professor Joseph Fletcher (1955 and 1969), then Professor of Social Ethics and Moral Philosophy at the Episcopal Theological School, Cambridge, Massachusetts.[3] It is proposed to examine these four essays in some detail.

Voluntary euthanasia

First of all it is desirable to confine attention to the question of *voluntary* euthanasia in adults, a point made by Flew in his opening paragraph in which he stated that no contributor to Downing's book proposed involuntary euthanasia, the person being unable to express a 'strong, constant and unequivocably expressed wish' to die. This was not in fact correct, for in the same volume Fletcher supported the practice of euthanasia for those who had never stated their wishes and were past making a mentally competent choice. For these Fletcher coined a phrase, not used by any other writer, of 'indirect euthanasia'. These dying persons could, he considered, be dealt with in three ways. Although unable to signify even agreement Fletcher suggested that their life could be terminated by (1) stopping treatment that prolonged life or (2) stopping all treatment or (3) giving a lethal drug with intent to kill.[4] All this, even the latter, he called indirect euthanasia, which appears to be a curious use of the term indirect. I would prefer the term non-voluntary euthanasia.

The right to die

Let us disregard these three red herrings, as others apparently have, and concentrate attention on the principle of *voluntary* euthanasia in an adult person of rational mind, examining first of all a person's right to die. This covers the whole question of suicide but it will be impossible to discuss so large an issue here. Instead let us consider one aspect of the question of suicide, a person's right to choose death when he is seriously ill. It is claimed that serious physical illness might be an extenuating circumstance for suicide. If this were conceded it would clearly involve three supplementary questions, first concerning the severity of the physical illness, secondly how near the person was to the time of death, and thirdly whether a distinction could be made between physical and mental illness. Thus many might consider that it was justifiable for someone who was dying of painful widespread cancer to ask for death to be expedited but not, say, for a violin player who had a permanent paralysis of his right hand and was unable to play his beloved instrument. Others feel that voluntary euthanasia might be justified in a physical illness, like cancer, but not in a mental illness such as manic psychosis.

In his article on 'The Patient's Right to Die' Fletcher did not define the categories of patients who had this alleged right, nor how they would exercise it. Instead he told four anecdotes[5] to illustrate his approach to the problem. Two stories concerned patients who had long-standing permanent severe brain damage; they were in no pain but were either unconscious or speechless and could not express their wishes for, or against, euthanasia. A third story concerned a man said to be slowly dying from pneumonia, although no grounds for this gloomy prognosis of certain death were stated nor were there any details of the nature of the infection nor of the antibiotics employed. Apparently he had been put into a mechanical respirator, an extremely unusual procedure in pneumonia. It was not stated if he was conscious and could communicate his wishes. The debated question was whether to turn off the respirator and discontinue the oxygen or even to let him continue dying slowly. Without consulting the wife who was waiting outside the ward, or attempting to ask the patient, the doctors asked a visiting clergyman whether they should stop the respirator and the oxygen. He agreed. The doctors then turned off all the apparatus, meanwhile the chaplain was told to inform the waiting wife: 'We are doing everything we can.' The patient meanwhile had died. After this hair-raising account of the care of the dying and the consolation of the relatives, there followed the fourth anecdote, written to illustrate a patient's right to choose death. This told of a woman dying from many secondary cancer tumours in her bones. She was the only person in the four anecdotes concerning whom there was any suggestion of pain, for she had 'agonizing shaking attacks . . . and little bits of her bones were splintering all the time'. (This is a lurid travesty of the pathological features that may occasionally occur in secondary cancer tumours in bones.) Even she did not complain of pain and did not ask explicitly for euthanasia. Instead she asked her husband 'I ought to die. Why can't I die?' The husband was depicted as speechless and unable to reply. He could have replied with considerable truth 'In the terminal stage of cancer, patients are not kept alive by drugs; they are kept alive by food and drink and it is I who have been giving you food and you who have been asking for it.'

Fletcher then commented, perhaps more truly than he realized 'It is the living who fear death, not the dying.' Too true; indeed in all four anecdotes it was the anguish of the relatives that was depicted; the patients had no agony apart from one woman dying of cancer. It is the relatives who are more likely, out of deep compassion, to ask for euthanasia to be administered to a patient who has never taken the initiative, and requested it. This is said not to dismiss, as with a trick, the problem of voluntary euthanasia; it is mentioned to highlight its complexity.

In old age death can be accepted as natural both by the patient and the relatives; it must be otherwise in the prime of life. Quite apart from the question of physical pain and distress, the relatives know that the loved one is going and a deep bond will soon be broken. Many say that the loved one will cease to be. Anyone, be it the patient who is dying or the relative who visits him, who in the prime of life can regard this prospect with calm serenity, has not tasted the richness of life. It cannot be otherwise.

In the four anecdotes, just mentioned, only one patient was conscious and could in any sense have exercised any choice of the alleged right to die. In his earlier essay, written in 1955, Fletcher had set forth in a more comprehensive manner the problems of euthanasia. Therein he had restricted his enquiries to the question of 'easing into death a patient suffering from a painful and fatal disease'. He inferred, but did not state clearly, that he was speaking only of a patient exercising a right to die *when death was near*. This was for him a human and a moral right. He definitely hoped that the right to die would *not* be extended to non-fatal illnesses.[6] He did not discuss the question of someone who was seriously, and even incurably, mentally distressed exercising a right to die; that is what usually leads to suicide.

A basic human right?

What kind of right is proposed? Is it a basic human right, comparable to those declared in the United Nations Charter of Human Rights? This stated that a person has a right to life, liberty, employment, leisure, education and medical attention. The so-called right to die has not been recorded among these human rights, but many would consider that it is in line with the modern wave of humanitarian thought that is rightly sensitive to all forms of suffering. Some thousands of English people, supporters of voluntary euthanasia, petitioned unsuccessfully the United Nations for recognition of the 'right of incurable sufferers to voluntary euthanasia' referring to Article 5 of the Declaration which stated: 'No one shall be subjected to torture.' This however was to extend the concept of torture beyond its common usage.

A legal right?

The legal difficulty of recognizing a right to die consists in the fact there is a far more fundamental and opposite declaration concerning the right to live. This underlies the laws of all communities, it forbids murder and manslaughter. Should there be any exceptions to this rule? If so, they should be most carefully defined and there should be stringent safeguards. Murderers are no longer condemned to death in Britain; even they have a right to life. War is the only commonly recognized denial of the right to life, even if some of us are dubious of its ethic. Apart from this a person has an absolute right to life. This is a human right, an inherent part of our basic condition; every other right to liberty, education, employment and so forth is dependent on life. It is also a moral right, which signifies that it is wrong to deprive a man of his life. It is also a legal right, which means that the whole weight of the law must be thrown against anyone, even doctors, who deprive a person of his life.

No one learned in law has proposed that it would be possible to give anyone a *legal right* to die. Some have gone further and seen the difficulty of a law recognizing even a *human* right to die. Thus Glanville Williams, an eminent legal authority and a firm supporter of voluntary euthanasia, criticized earlier bills on euthanasia when in 1958 he wrote:

The previous bills would have created what may be called a human right to euthanasia. Under the present suggestion no patient would have a right to euthanasia; it would be in the discretion of his doctor to agree or disagree.[7]

Instead his legislative suggestion would have restored 'personal liberty in a field in which men differ on the question of conscience'.[8]

Legal duties

Williams with his knowledge of law knew that legal rights confer legal duties from which exemption can be claimed only on grounds of conscience. Previous bills on voluntary euthanasia, which had in his opinion 'created what may be called a human right to euthanasia', did not actually confer a 'positive duty (on the patient's doctor) to do an act that might be against his conscience'.[9] Williams left it an open question whether if the administration of euthanasia was *not* against the conscience of the doctor, then he would be under some obligation of contract and professional responsibility, if not common humanity, to co-operate and administer euthanasia, if this was requested.

Williams and the supporters of voluntary euthanasia have been silent on this important point. Unless the doctor can plead conscience, is he then under some obligation to co-operate in the administration of voluntary euthanasia, if an act has been passed by the legislature? What if the doctor considers by reason of his professional *knowledge* that the patient is not near unto death? Is this doctor to be exempted? For instance, under the terms of the Voluntary Euthanasia Bill (1969) what would have been the position of a doctor who found that a person was suffering from a non-fatal disease, but one without remedy and likely to cause distress? Would the doctor be in a position to refuse euthanasia on a question of knowledge rather than that of conscience? Perhaps, if this Bill had been passed, it would become common knowledge that a certain doctor had administered voluntary euthanasia to a few persons in the terminal stage of inoperable cancer; if so the doctor would have difficulty in pleading objections of conscience to voluntary euthanasia as a general principle. Could the doctor then refuse what might be crudely called 'death on demand' if the patient could obtain one medical certificate from a consultant stating that he had an irremediable disease likely to cause him distress? Clearly much more thought is required by those who support, and by those who oppose voluntary euthanasia, before there can be any legal recognition of the right to die.

To give but one example, the commonest cause of death in Britain is a slow progressive degeneration of the arteries, called atheroma, or, because accompanied by hardening of the arteries, atherosclerosis. Atheroma is the cause of coronary heart disease, of most strokes and many other conditions such as senile dementia. At the time of writing (1973), it is regarded as incurable and no cause has been demonstrated. It starts soon after birth or during childhood and adolescence and slowly but to a variable degree affects almost everyone. Men are affected more than women, so that the former do not usually live as long as the latter. Most adults could be certified to have atheroma, an irremediable disease likely to cause them distress if they live long enough. If a patient in the prime of life developed signs suggestive of heart disease and was referred to a consultant, who attributed the condition to early signs of coronary heart disease, but no heart failure or thrombosis or angina, and the patient hearing that atheroma was incurable, demanded euthanasia, could his own medical practitioner refuse to accede to this 'death on demand', when some consultant had certified correctly the presence of an irremediable condition, one likely to cause distress?

A human right?

Even if it is impossible to recognize a legal right to die, what is to be understood as a *human* right to die? Is it to be compared to the acceptable human rights to life, liberty and leisure? Clearly those who support legislation on voluntary euthanasia wish for some wide recognition of the human right to die. This however is a vague term, it is necessary to clarify this demand. Clearly everyone will die in the end; in a sense no one will be denied this right eventually.

There is however a natural desire to die under certain conditions and not under others. People do not wish to be kept alive if the quality of life is poor, especially if life is dependent on special machines or elaborate treatment. This is generally recognized as an ethically permissible request. It has been specifically deemed permissible by pronouncements from the Pope, it has become standard medical teaching at all British teaching hospitals not to prolong life under all circumstances and at all costs, so that there is really no need to press for legal reform in this respect. This is not to claim that when an old person gets a heart attack the decision, whether to resuscitate or not to resuscitate, is infallible in every case. All decisions are subject to error. People do not want elaborate investigations or meddlesome treatment merely to extend life at all costs, especially when a person is nearing death either by reason of age or because of incurable disease. In other words, people desire to die naturally. All this is understandable and it is right.

Patients and their families should feel free to discuss these matters with their doctors: they should exercise their rights by not signing consent forms to heroic operations under all circumstances. They may even sign a general statement to this effect which can guide their doctors and family if they are themselves unable to do so because of illness or old age (see Appendix D).

It is however quite a different matter to say that they do not wish to be kept alive by giving fluids to relieve thirst. If these were withheld death would occur in a week. They would not wish to be refused all foods because these keep people alive. If no food at all were taken most elderly or sick persons would be dead within thirty days, but many of them would suffer unnecessarily the pangs of hunger.

Everyone has a natural hope that they will live into their seventies if not eighties, provided they remain fit in body and alert in mind, and then they will die quickly and quietly, perhaps in their sleep, without pain or much illness, and certainly not as a burden to other people. This is most understandable. It is however a part of our human predicament that we cannot ensure this kind of death. One doctor who supported euthanasia actually envisaged people choosing some arbitrary date, such as 75, and dying then even if body and mind were fit.[10] This seems to be the logical outcome of an insistence on a right to die without disability or disease, but it cannot be regarded as death without mental distress in the mind of the person about to die. Condemned prisoners and those about to commit suicide reveal the anguish that accompanies a decision to die. The decision to die at 75 will certainly not solve the problem of a quiet serene deathbed, for the majority of men and women in Britain die of disease several years before they reach 75. Even if the age limit were dropped to 68 for men and 74 for women (because this is the average life expectancy at birth in Britain), it still means that half the population will have died of disease before reaching this age.

It is a part of our human predicament that we cannot determine the date of our death unless we decide it by choosing suicide. To avoid all pain one should never be born. After all a baby has a natural human right not to receive a great deal of pain when he is being born, but severe pain and great pressure on the skull, lasting for several hours, are a part of every birth except those of Caesarean section. Has every babe therefore a human right to Caesarean section? Should not a compassionate mother insist on the human right of her babe to painless birth? I am afraid we have to accept our human predicament and realize too that unless the baby does greet the world with a cry (and he will often be smacked until he does so), he will not breathe and he will not live. If the mother is given too much sedative for too long and this sedative reaches the baby before birth, he may be sedated so much that he will not cry, but will die. Throughout life it is a part of our human predicament that we cannot exercise full control over the accidents that may maim us for life and the diseases which may cause disability and death. All we can do is to decrease the accidents and the diseases as far as possible by careful thought. We cannot opt out of pain and distress. They are a part of life. We have no human right to be without pain and distress, we can only plan to decrease them. We have a human right to hope that death, like life, will be as painless as possible; we have no human right to demand it at all costs.

A liberty to commit suicide?

It has still to be argued, and this not on religious grounds, important as they are to many of us, whether a person has a human right to choose death, for it is on this that the whole weight of the argument in favour of voluntary euthanasia is based. As usually stated the question has a fundamental confusion of thought, for the Suicide Act of 1961 recognizes that in England and Wales a person has a liberty, but not a right, to choose to end his own life. He has however no right in England and Wales to ask for assistance in his suicide from anyone else, since in this country it is still an offence to aid, abet or counsel suicide.

There is a firm distinction in law and in practice between rights and liberties. A person has a right to life and can invoke the protection of the homicide act and the assistance of the police in any attempt to deny him the right to life. A person has a right to freedom of speech and political assembly, and the law recognizes and is prepared to support these legal rights. The law also recognizes certain liberties; thus it recognizes the liberty of a woman to act as a prostitute, it recognizes the liberty of two consenting adults to indulge in homosexual practices. In these and other liberties the law does not restrain persons from exercising these liberties, but it does not assist them. Further it will not defend these liberties in the court; thus no legal action is possible by a prostitute to recover fees for services rendered. Liberties are not enforced by the courts; rights can be enforced. Glanville Williams indicated this distinction when, speaking of legislation on voluntary euthanasia, he said it would 'restore personal liberty in a field in which men differ on the question of conscience'.[11]

Involvement of the medical profession

The question whether a person has a 'right to die' not only conceals the confusion between liberties and rights; it shirks the main issues as far as the medical profession is concerned. The question is not merely whether the patient has the right not only to choose death, but to demand that he be granted by his doctor facilities for suicide. It goes still further and asks whether the patient has the right to ask from his doctor not only assistance in suicide, wherein the patient swallows his own lethal tablets, but the termination of a patient's life by some positive action, probably an injection.

The administration of the Abortion Act (1967) has demonstrated how difficult it is to legislate concerning what categories of persons are entitled to termination of pregnancy. There has been all the difficulty, if not the impossibility, of saying whether the pregnant mother had a physical disease which would be aggravated by pregnancy; it has proved impossible to state what mental conditions justified termination; these might vary from a natural anxiety over an unwanted pregnancy to a severe psychosis. Many patients had a condition partly physical, partly psychological, but the Act forced doctors to certify either physical disease such as German measles or mental disease, such as a psychosis. Mental disorders were certified in about 60% of terminations. Other terminations were allowed on social grounds, the plea being made that other members of the woman's family might suffer. All this meant that, in practice, any woman who had the necessary money could obtain the two essential medical certificates. It amounted to termination on demand, at least for the wealthy.

It is probable that the enactment of any legislation on voluntary euthanasia would have exactly the same result. It would prove impossible to define the categories of persons who were entitled to ask for euthanasia and for whom two doctors, one being of consultant status, could certify that there were adequate grounds for euthanasia. Since all illness in a person has a physical and a psychological aspect, it would prove impossible to allow voluntary euthanasia to those suffering from a physical condition such as cancer and to deny it to those suffering from the more severe and more prolonged pain of mental depression. Since all illness in a person has its social aspects and involves relatives in particular and society in general, it would prove impossible to define whether there are social grounds, as in the case of the Abortion Act, on which voluntary euthanasia should be permitted. May an elderly person, who is a burden to her resentful daughter, state this openly as the major reason for her petition for voluntary euthanasia? Is this any less painful than the depression of a mental illness or the pangs of terminal cancer? After all, the person could argue that it was her life which was at stake; why should anyone else have the power, or the right, to veto her decision? There would be no question of the involvement of a second, dependent, potential life, such as that present when the termination of pregnancy is considered. Any legislation on voluntary euthanasia, however carefully worded, would mean death on demand, at the hands of the medical profession. This point was clearly acknowledged by a consultant psychiatrist from the Maudsley Hospital, an open supporter of the Voluntary Euthanasia Society, when I debated the issue with him at the London Hospital in 1971. He supported the notion of death on demand, if the demand was a rational one and a sustained wish. He even stated that his own death, say in the ensuing week, would not be a matter for undue regret or distress, but I did not debate this point with him. Instead we retired to dinner with the students and drank to one another's very good health.

Family and friends

The question about whether a person has a human right to die has a fatal individualist slant: it envisages the solitary patient wracked with pain debating to be or not to be. I would not choose to defend against all comers the proposition that a man, having no friends and no family, and who was living on a desert island, especially if he had no belief in God, had no human right to choose death. Obviously he could not ask anyone to assist him to die; no one else would even be involved in an act which signified a measure of agreement in his death, no one else would mourn his death or bury him. Alone he lived; alone he would die.

On the other hand anyone who lives in a community, having kith and kin, friends and neighbours, has no human right to choose death if in so doing he is considering only the effect on himself. He has no human right to disregard the effect of his death on other persons. This argument is as broad as it is long; perhaps they will be glad if he goes, perhaps he has been a burden to them, he can leave the money to them sooner, they will no longer have to bear the mental agony of witnessing his pain and distress. Perhaps however they will grieve at his going and feel they are losing a loved one. It will be difficult to strike the profit and loss account among all these imponderables. One thing that seems abundantly clear is the human obligation to discuss matters with kith and kin. Many would go further and say that he is under a moral obligation to discuss matters with them and to gain if possible their agreement. Any discussion with relatives would inevitably turn considerably on a question of the certainty of the diagnosis and the prognosis of any disease that is present, and so the doctor cannot stand completely outside the matter.

The supporters of voluntary euthanasia appear crassly ignorant of, or shockingly insensitive to, the rights of the relatives and friends of anyone considering his own euthanasia. In the first Euthanasia Bill (1936) the position of the relatives was given legal status, the specified next of kin had to be informed, a legally constituted court could hear objections before it decided whether to accede to the petition for euthanasia. In the Voluntary Euthanasia Bill (1969) there was no recognition at all of relatives; the person applying for euthanasia was under no legal obligation to discuss the matter with them, the doctor was under no obligation to mention either the petition for euthanasia or the fact of its administration to family, relatives or friends.

No reference to the natural rights of relatives has been traced in the recent literature of the Voluntary Euthanasia Society.[12] The theologian Joseph Fletcher never refers to the rights of the relatives in agreeing to the voluntary euthanasia. One would have appreciated from the supporters of voluntary euthanasia some discussion of the human rights of relatives, some necessity of discussing the termination of life with those with whom one has shared the deepest of all experiences. If there is any reference to this in the recent euthanasia literature I have not found it. This surprises me because it must be clearly stated that those who support voluntary euthanasia are deeply sensitive to physical suffering.

At the same time it must be recorded that the supporters of voluntary euthanasia are either incredibly naive or obtusely ignorant of the mental suffering of someone debating in his own mind to be or not to be, also the distress of the relatives who enter into this debate. Motives will become incredibly mixed, an endless debate about 'what is best' will burden the minds of all.

During my thirty years as a doctor and again in work at Telephone Samaritans, and also in my ten years' work as hospital chaplain where I witnessed the resuscitation of many persons who had attempted suicide, I can say that great mental agony usually accompanies any decision to die, unless one is aged or near to death by reason of serious physical disease. The desire for life seems built into the very core of our being; without this as the most profound instinct it is difficult to know how human beings, even the higher mammals, would have survived on this planet. As a built-in part of the human mind, it seems to me that the fear of death and the desire for self-preservation must be fundamental and far stronger than the sexual impulse. From our earliest years we have learned by instinct and experience to shun danger and death. When in perfect health and still young in years, a person may say that he will eventually choose death calmly and objectively, but when he is existentially linked to the decision about death, it is otherwise. He shakes; he trembles; he dithers; he makes a decision and then retracts.

Repugnance to the taking of life

To conclude: the question whether a person has a right to die has a smirking insincerity concealed in its euphemistic phraseology. Right sounds a noble sentiment, the right to die calls to mind those who die for their country or for their political faith or for their ideals. It is the stuff of warriors and martyrs. But the right to die, when applied to sick persons, is something fundamentally different, and it conceals the fact that it is really an argument about whether one has a right to get someone else to do the killing; and that someone is the doctor who will cast a cloak of respectability, if not anonymity, over the whole act.

From the dawn of history to the present day, all peoples, of whatever race, religion and political outlook have always felt the greatest horror, if not repugnance, in killing someone else. It is true that this repugnance is overcome in time of war especially if the enemy is unseen; even in times of peace it may be suddenly extinguished when overcome by the deeper instinct of self-preservation. The present generation have shown great compassion in deciding for the first time in history that it is repugnant for anyone to kill any other person, even a murderer. When I was a young medical officer in Kenya it fell to my lot to attend the hanging of condemned prisoners. The actual fall may be extremely swift, and death almost instantaneous; but the man struggling when the noose is placed round his neck can never, never be forgotten. After death it fell to the medical officer to certify death by examination of the warm body. The effect on all the participants in the prison cannot be described to anyone who has never been present.

It is right that a doctor should feel the greatest repulsion to the question of killing one of his own patients. All his professional instincts, all his human compassion has striven to maintain the life of those who entrust themselves to his hands. That one of his patients, who has a fatal irremediable complaint, but who has weeks or months of life still before him, should have the right to ask his doctor for termination, and that the doctor should be under some obligation to accede to this request, seems specially abhorrent.

The doctor has seen other patients with the same complaint, even with more distress, who have put up a brave encounter. It is somewhat of a slur on the doctor's professional skill to have another patient ask for death, when life still holds many periods of possible enjoyment. What will be the position of the doctor who does not agree that the condition of the patient justifies the request for death? What if he has doubts about diagnosis or prognosis? Must he refer the patient to another doctor, or doctors, until eventually one is found who will agree? It is to be hoped that the question of fees will not enter these transactions; for human nature being what it is, fees influence decisions in many persons. Even doctors cannot claim complete moral rectitude or scientific objectivity. They are human.

It would be a sad day for the medical profession if any or many of its members did not have this horror of killing a person. Such doctors should never give an anaesthetic in which a person is taken almost to the jaws of death, and brought back again; they should never be asked to look after patients having irremediable complaints. After all it is not very gratifying to a doctor to visit day after day those whom he cannot cure, especially if there is much distress only partially alleviated by medical treatment. It is but easy and natural under these circumstances for the doctor to look forward to the man's death, even counsel it, even administer it. I have on many occasions felt thus myself. No longer will the doctor have to call by day and continue the deceptive charade, jollying the man along; noting the strained look on the faces of the relatives. It is not easy to visit night after night someone whose fate mocks all one's scientific skills. All this could be solved once and for all if the person had signed some advance declaration in favour of euthanasia. The patient would only have to nod his head, and heads do nod in sleep. Then perhaps he would sleep for ever, and everything should be at the discretion of the doctor. Should it?

Medical objections

Before discussing the ethical basis of the patient's alleged right to die, it is essential to weigh the reasons which forbid for all time and in all circumstances the patient's medical practitioner from any association with legalized voluntary euthanasia. The doctor who looks after a patient must never be associated with euthanasia and the patient must know this. The six points which follow do not rest on religious beliefs, however important or unimportant some of us consider these to be; they rest on facts and attitudes which are built into the doctor-patient relationship; especially as it is seen in the care for the enfeebled, the elderly and the dying.

First of all, it is seldom certain, beyond any reasonable doubt, that the patient will not subsequently change his mind and cancel his request for euthanasia. Have other drugs, other doctors, other nurses been tried? Perhaps they will be more skilful in relieving the pain and the patient will find life worth living. There are institutions in which there is almost always success in alleviating the pain and distress of terminal cancer: if the patient was transferred there, would he change his mind? Then again psychiatrists who have observed patients during the terminal stages of fatal illness stress the changing moods vacillating between denial and acceptance, changing between hope and despair. Few patients have a steady constant desire to die, save perhaps in the last illness of an aged person quietly accepting death.

Secondly, even if the nearest of kin and the closest relatives have agreed to the euthanasia and discussed it with the patient, bereavement brings such emotional trauma that those who are left are often full of recrimination, guilt and anger. These feelings are even at present often directed against the doctor. The relatives may consider that they never gave consent to the euthanasia. They may spread dangerous malicious gossip; they may take legal proceedings especially in the light of the findings reported at the post-mortem examination.

Thirdly, the doctor knows more clearly than anyone else that any decision about euthanasia must be based on a firm statement of the diseases present. From his student days he has attended too many autopsies where even the most eminent consultants have been confounded. Yet he dare not disclose to the patient and the relatives the measure of his uncertainty, without undermining confidence. Perhaps he has to name the diseases present on some written report; if this is not done the relatives may give a garbled account of the medical indications for euthanasia; if this is done then diseases stated to be present during life can be checked against those found at any autopsy and written in the death certificate. There will inevitably be many surprises.

Fourthly, even if all the medical facts are correctly known, the doctor can never be certain that the external circumstances which are the basis of the choice for euthanasia will not change. A decision to die is always taken against a social background of certain circumstances and the most unpredictable events may occur, perhaps when it is too late to reverse the decision about euthanasia. One illustration from my personal experience will be given.

Over forty years ago I was a government medical officer in charge of a small hospital in East Africa and there was admitted under my care a young single Frenchman who had tried to commit suicide. When his personal affairs became too complex and distressing he placed a revolver to the right side of his chest and fired a bullet. This missed his heart but went through his spinal cord, severing it completely so that there was no sensation or movement below the waist. A surgical colleague explored the wound: it was evident that there would be no recovery as the spinal cord had been completely severed. He would never walk again and never control the use of his bladder. Those were the days when it fell invariably to the doctor to pass the catheter and draw off the urine. I got to know him well as several times a day I passed the instrument up to his bladder, realizing that sooner or later I would cause a urinary infection which eventually would kill him. In those days that was the invariable fate of anyone who had to have the urine drawn off at frequent intervals through a catheter. There were no consultants in those parts of Africa in those days.

There had been but a brief reply to the cable sent to his parents in France, but then we had not given details of his injuries, leaving that to letters which in those days took three weeks to reach Europe by boat. A reply took six weeks to be received. When my patient knew his fate, that he would never walk again, never work, never play and never make love, he repeatedly asked to die. He refused to see friends and was estranged from the religion of his forefathers. But he would talk to me at the many sessions when I seized the member that was dead and pushed up the catheter. Here was an irremediable condition, proved beyond any doubt. Here was a man who had shown in his action and words his desire to die. It would be a mercy. But I had to cover my tracks; I had to start a course of injections, which I gave in privacy, and wherein I controlled the dose and the content. So I agreed and started the injections of a cumulative drug.

Then in the second month after the accident the letters started coming, for a boat had reached Mombasa. His parents accepted all that had happened. His mother wanted to nurse him till he died; his father sent money for the passage and salary for a nurse to accompany him on the boat. Then we both became very, very frightened. Had he received too many injections? But we got him home to France; he wrote letters of gratitude, so did his parents. Maybe he had wasted his substance with riotous living in a far country, but he had come home. After several months he died painlessly of his urinary infection. Circumstances change decisions, decisions to die, and who can predict these changes?

Fifthly, in practical terms the doctor is the last person to administer euthanasia. He has become mentally conditioned by reason of long habits; he cannot regard the matter impartially, or consider the issue fairly, or perform the act calmly. His professional training has been canalized into the protection of life and the enrichment of its quality. He has an inbred respect for human life, speaking of the sanctity of life. This is the ultimate basis of the only creed that most doctors understand.

He has acted as counsel for the defence of the life of his client, he cannot easily reverse his role and become prosecutor for the sentence of death. He cannot sit calmly in judgment on this schizophrenic split in his own personality and his roles, acting as judge and summing up the evidence for and against the termination of life, and as jury giving the verdict – and even acting as executioner. He cannot be prosecutor, defender, judge, jury and executioner all in one person. He will polarize to one role or other. It will be a sad day for many of his patients if he polarizes too easily towards termination. Every doctor in general practice has a score or more of incurable patients on his books, consuming to little purpose his time, ability and patience. Some doctors are naturally pessimists, some have morbid minds, and some develop insanity. It would be a dishonourable day for any doctor if a crop of unexpected euthanasias were the first sign of commencing insanity. The press and television would not be slow to publicize the news. On the other hand many doctors would polarize towards a humane if not a sentimental regard for life and would refuse almost all applications for euthanasia. Would the suffering patient then constitute a hard-luck case and be highlighted by publicity, such as occurred when the termination of pregnancy was refused to a girl of 12 years of age? Must some other doctor, even a private clinic, then be sought? Do private clinics charge fees, payable by the estate? It would indeed be difficult to say what scale of fees could be charged, and the relatives who would inherit would be in some straits to judge aright. Pressures would rocket the fees, as the patients became more and more distressed.

Sixthly, the whole basis of medical practice is built on a position of trust. There has been an agreement to be a patient and an agreement to be the doctor, but more than an agreement. There has been a contract to be a patient and to be the doctor, but more than a contract. One reaches round for some other word, signifying a deep and abiding trust between the two parties. Patient and doctor have *covenanted* to keep faith for better for worse, in sickness and in health, till the gates of death do them part. This deserves a chapter on its own to elaborate it, for herein lies the heart of the euthanasia problem.

If any country should ever be so unwise as to enact legislation on voluntary euthanasia, these six weighty reasons, which rest on no foundation of religion or private system of ethics, demand that the patient's own doctor, and any consultant or specialist with whom this doctor may confer, must stand for all time and in all circumstances completely outside any question of euthanasia. They must never be even a party to advising the patient, let alone facilitating, his legalized application for assisted suicide. *Doctors, all persons designated as doctors, must be completely excluded from the role of the person who terminates life.* The public must know this for all time and for all places and for all circumstances.

If the patient, under any legislation permitting voluntary euthanasia, ever wishes to exercise his liberty to choose death, then this patient must choose someone who has been designated by the state for this purpose, someone distinct in title, office and function from any of the regular members of the medical profession. The first Euthanasia Bill (1936) envisaged the appointment of recognized, qualified euthanasists to assess the claims of applicants and to administer euthanasia under due safeguards. Who these persons should be and whether they should have medical training, must be left to those who support voluntary euthanasia. Perhaps one day there will be duly appointed euthanasists and Punch will hope that there are not too many enthusiastic euthanasists.

The medical covenant

The whole basis of medical practice is built on a basis of trust, a covenant of confidence,[13] to which there are no exceptions. The patient and the doctor enter into a mutual relationship of great intimacy, and one characterized by trust. Among all the diverse relationships that men make, one with another, it is almost unique. Other relationships are established between man and man; one thinks of master and servant, solicitor and client, priest and parishioner; all of these are voluntary associations. It is quite inadequate to speak of these associations in terms of a contract; they are not business deals to deliver certain specified goods by a certain date if an agreed sum of money is paid. These are covenanted associations, two persons agreeing together for a specific purpose, which is clearly recognized on both sides. The solicitor cannot guarantee the client that he will achieve success in the law courts, but he does undertake to espouse all his interests. He asks for and respects confidences. The priest cannot assure any member of his flock of definite benefits, but he is under an obligation to respect the secrecy of the confessional, and concerning this there is an honoured tradition not only in the Catholic Church but in other Christian churches, and one carefully maintained in all religious faiths.

The peculiarity of the doctor-patient relationship is that it can only operate if the patient entrusts body and mind without reserve into the hands of the doctor, doing this for health and healing. The patient must be able at all times to feel that his doctor will act as the guardian of life: they must keep company and keep faith when illness clouds the patient's judgment and fears gain an upper hand. The patient must never, never be able to feel in the dark watches of the night that his own covenanted companion in the mutual search for health has slowly been accumulating the evidence, in terms of blood pressure and blood counts, which could, at the drop of a hat, be dramatically produced as evidence of incurable disease, that is, a justification of euthanasia. The doctor might never discuss all this damning data with the patient concerned, but this would only intensify the morbid midnight phantasies that the medical practitioner might broach the matter with a spouse or relative whom he would then bind to secrecy, in the alleged interests of the patient. With complete sincerity the doctor could maintain that he was merely giving some preliminary warning to the spouse that the position was not at present quite hopeless, but that it would be so within a short time. Another X-ray, another blood test, would settle the matter. So the two persons, practitioner and spouse, would conspire together, in the interests of the ailing patient, and the mere fact that both denied this when questioned by the sufferer, would not merely heighten the tension, it would deepen the distrust. Patient, spouse and doctor would then be caught in a trap, out of which there would be no escape, without a complete loss of confidence on all sides. They would be locked irrevocably in a position of hopeless duplicity.

If a country ever enacts legislation on voluntary euthanasia, it will be essential that the patient should choose some other person, someone who has never been associated with his own medical practitioner, to determine if he might be a candidate qualifying for euthanasia. To do otherwise is to destroy the foundation on which patient and doctor covenant together to seek health and happiness.

VII

Recent Developments

Report of British Medical Association: reply of Voluntary Euthanasia Society

In January 1971 the British Medical Association issued a report (printed below as Appendix A) condemning voluntary euthanasia on many grounds, and a leading article in the *British Medical Journal*[1] reviewed the numerous arguments set forth in some detail in this book. The report did not discuss the legal and ethical objections; it stressed the impossibility of providing adequate safeguards and pointed out that legislation would lay a serious 'oppression on the confused, sensitive and perhaps weakened minds of apprehensive suffering patients', especially if they were elderly. In the same issue of the journal, by a felicitous coincidence, Sir George Pickering, formerly Regius Professor of Medicine at the University of Oxford, wrote: 'I reject euthanasia – killing people is not what doctors should, or could, do.'[2]

On the whole the report was well received in the national press and in the medical journals, except possibly the *Medical Tribune*, whose editor was known to favour voluntary euthanasia. He had contributed a masterly essay on the history of suicide and voluntary euthanasia in a book which advocated legislation.[3] He had indeed been able to write an editorial article condemning the report even before it was published,[4] thereby displaying an unusual degree of foresight. An article by a Huddersfield general practitioner in that same issue of the journal advocated that people should

opt for death at, say 75, rather than peter out in increasing dependence on others; . . . the day will come when we should be able to say, cheerfully, without incurring the distaste of our fellows or the interference of psychiatrists, 'I am expecting to die next year,' exactly as today we say, 'So-and-so is expecting to give birth in the near future.'

In another medical journal,[5] which rather enjoys acting as an able critic of the medical establishment, a woman journalist who was not medically qualified wrote with considerable perception and sensitivity about the problems raised in long illness. She professed her point of view, if not her creed, when she stated: 'I believe in voluntary euthanasia,' and added: 'The literature of the Voluntary Euthanasia Society contains all the legal aspects and expert opinions for and against the reform I want to see.' She most forcefully accused the doctors of complete failure to discuss the matter. It is hoped that this book of mine has at least broken the silence; but only at considerable cost, for many reading this book will conclude that death can be at times a grim affair, and it is absolutely certain that portions of the book will be lifted out of their context, quoted and misquoted by a few of those who support legislation on voluntary euthanasia.

Having said this, I feel I must state once more that in all my dealings with the Voluntary Euthanasia Society, and in every public debate with several of their officers, I have been offered every courtesy. These are very high-minded persons, genuinely moved by the fact that mortal illness is often a tragic affair. I venture to observe that it can only be transformed by the amazing deepening of the spirit of the dying person. I have been very conscious of this on several occasions in my thirty years of medical practice. This, after all, is the only thing which can redeem a dark situation, a point to which I wish to return at the end of this chapter. The officers of the Society are genuinely concerned at the amount of suffering that is present. After careful and sincere thought they consider that legislation on voluntary euthanasia would provide the best solution. That it is not always the best solution is shown by a statement made to me by Lord Raglan after we had debated the issue at the University of Sussex in 1970, one year after he had introduced his Bill into the House of Lords. He said he would not endeavour to introduce a similar bill on any subsequent occasion, but was glad that he had ventilated the matter. This highlights the difficulties of solving the problem by legislation.

To my mind it is a pity that the few doctors who support the Society are not more vocal in its support. In my reply to the woman journalist just quoted, I challenged the respected members of the medical profession who are said to support the proposal (of voluntary euthanasia) with the assertion that 'they never give us facts and figures on the number of persons requesting euthanasia on which to base our opinions. I repeat never.' No doctor took up the challenge. I went on to challenge any doctor to say whether he supported the practice of voluntary euthanasia for the categories of persons mentioned in the 1969 Bill, since 'it can be safely asserted, without fear of medical contradiction, that the majority of middle-aged persons have at least one, and often several, incurable physical disorders which are likely to cause severe distress if they live several more years'.[6] All of these could have qualified for voluntary euthanasia under the 1969 Bill. No doctor took up the challenge, and the only local member of the Society, a doctor of outstanding skill and impeccable ethical standards, has found himself too busy on several occasions to discuss the matter with me.

The Voluntary Euthanasia Society considered the report of the British Medical Association and in due course issued a carefully stated rejoinder (printed below as Appendix B). It contended that the BMA report denied the right to 'self-determination'. Perhaps this could be stated more succinctly as the right to 'self-termination'. This book has argued that there is a personal liberty in England and Wales to commit suicide, but there never could be any legal right to suicide, for that would make it obligatory on the state to provide means to ensure that this legal right could be exercised. However many doctors had objections, by reason of conscience, to administering euthanasia, the state would have to find persons who would co-operate in administering euthanasia, be it some specially appointed doctor, or some other non-medical person, given special training in euthanasia. All this would place an intolerable burden on the state to ensure adequate safeguards. The reply of the Voluntary Euthanasia Society was:

If the safeguards proposed (including agreement between doctor and consultant) are not considered adequate, it should not be beyond the powers of the medical and legal professions to produce others which would be acceptable to the community.[7]

In the light of what is written in this book, one of the first books in recent years to discuss at all fully the problem of voluntary euthanasia, it will be interesting to see what proposals are set forward. Truly there is an inherent dilemma here.

Safeguards

Safeguards are essential in any legalization of voluntary euthanasia, but their content has never been discussed. The bare minimum is that in every case of voluntary euthanasia there should be a statement by two doctors, one being the general practitioner and the other the consultant, that certain diseases are considered to be present, that they are incurable and causing distress, that the patient appears to have a steady determined wish to die, that they consider him to be sane, and that he understands the nature of his request. These facts should be communicated to the appropriate authority. Further, in the interests of justice and future applicants for euthanasia, the patient should state that it is desirable for the facts concerning his illness to be checked at a post-mortem examination, which should follow every voluntary euthanasia, and would disclose which diseases actually were present. This knowledge is absolutely essential as a safeguard for the applicant, for the relatives, and for the community. Relatives have a right to know whether the recommendation was made on a correct estimate of the disease present. It should be clearly recognized that, at the present time, no legal action could be taken by relatives, or any other person, if errors in diagnosis had occurred, provided reasonable care and skill had been employed.

Doctors too, as a part of their scientific discipline, should also insist on the collection of these facts and the publication of scientific papers determining the degree of correspondence of the ante-mortem diagnosis, which constituted the medical basis to justify voluntary euthanasia, and the post-mortem findings to test its accuracy. Unless such a procedure is instituted there would be a tendency to cover up any deficiency of knowledge. If a body of scientific knowledge were built up in this way, facts would emerge such as, shall we say, an excellent correspondence of the ante-mortem and post-mortem reports in cancer, but a very low correspondence, as at present, in the diagnosis of a stroke (cerebral vascular accident). Armed with this knowledge doctors, relatives and prospective candidates would feel reassured if cancer was present, but more cautious if a stroke had occurred.

Yet any administrative procedure such as this would be certain to kill the practice of voluntary euthanasia, for doctors would be slow to disclose the areas of ignorance. It was explained earlier in this book that errors are often present in any clinical diagnosis, and the latter is often revised from time to time, until finally the patient is dying and now in a sense the diagnosis does not matter. When the patient is dying, it is usually too late to institute curative measures; it is too late to set the machinery of voluntary euthanasia in operation; it is too late for the patient to have any informed wishes in the matter.

It may come as a shock to many members of the general public to realize that doctors do not always understand fully the nature of any serious illness, or may not be able to detect all the unsuspected complications, but this is true. Let me give one example. It may be reasonably certain that a man has cancer of the lungs; he has been a heavy cigarette smoker, the X-ray appearance is conclusive, a small piece of cancerous tissue has been removed at a special examination called bronchoscopy, during which the surgeon has actually seen, through a long instrument, the tumour mass in the air-tube (bronchus). Having established the diagnosis, there is however no point in performing other examinations to see if there is arthritis of the hip, or any developing diabetes. The cancer is perhaps far too large to allow for any operation. So it is considered to be merely a question of time before the patient dies. A mild analgesic drug is taken and pain is relieved after only one tablet, but then a week later the patient has rather more pain, and his wife thinks that the doctor has said that the dose could be increased safely to two tablets if necessary. She gives two tablets, and the patient dies half an hour later. She will probably fear that she has killed her husband. A post-mortem examination however then reveals the two tablets in the stomach, almost undissolved, but also quite unexpectedly some coronary thrombosis, the commonest cause of sudden death in a man in the prime of life. Everyone then agrees that all has been for the best and the wife is immensely relieved. Neighbours, however, who have heard the story of the double dose, have already perhaps started a rumour that the doctor and the wife had agreed to terminate the life of the patient dying with cancer. In my experience, once a story like this starts in a village – and I was a village priest for ten years – the truth never catches up with rumour, never kills it. Even after the results of the post-mortem examination are known, people still nod their heads and wink at one another.

Do doctors practice euthanasia?

This brings us to the discussion of whether at the present time doctors are practising euthanasia, the termination of the life of a person. It is frequently alleged that this occurs, some say not infrequently. It is the basis of much that is written by those who support legislation on voluntary euthanasia. Certain opinion polls, which never define what they mean by euthanasia, or even voluntary euthanasia, have asked doctors to state if their colleagues are performing it, but never, as far as I am aware, have they asked if the doctor is practising it himself.[8]

The alleged results of these misleading opinion polls might lead us to believe that doctors are frequently performing euthanasia. In more than one medical journal I have challenged the doctors who support legislation on voluntary euthanasia to tell us how often patients in the prime of life ask in a determined sane manner for termination, but as far as I am aware, no single doctor has produced these figures. I would like in all confidence to ask them how often they took the law into their own hands, acting, I have no doubt at all, even if I cannot agree with their decision, out of motives of charity and compassion. I have offered to travel and meet these doctors. I have not succeeded in gaining an audience with anyone who admits that he practised voluntary euthanasia, except with a few doctors who admit to something which in my opinion is fundamentally and completely different, as I will discuss immediately – the administration of maximal sedation, to the restless body of a person whose mind is already dead.

In modern hospitals it should be possible to see that patients have little pain during the last stages of mortal illness. I do not say that this always occurs; there are failures, which will be discussed later in this chapter. Given the staff, the knowledge, and the compassion, all three being absolutely essential, no one should die in a modern hospital with much pain. I am satisfied both as a doctor and as a hospital chaplain that a painful death is seldom 'unavoidable. When it does occur it reflects some shortage of nurses, or some inexperience and lack of knowledge on the part of junior medical or surgical staff, some lack of experience or even some lack of sympathy.

On the other hand, in the difficult down-town sections of our modern cities and in the wide stretches of the countryside, personal observation shows me that people still die in their homes, sometimes in lamentable conditions. Let me say straight away that I think it is right and natural, if possible, for a person to die in his own house, surrounded by those who care for him and the surroundings of hearth and home. Some people insist on dying at home and some spouses insist on nursing those whom they love until they break under the load. I am fully satisfied that in a small proportion of these patients there comes a time when *the person has died* but the body goes on living. The person is dead: he can no longer speak, or hear, or talk rationally; his whole personality has broken up long ago, leaving only a shell of the former self. Eyes are blind, ears are deaf, lips are silent or mutter senseless phrases. The last intelligible words, have been spoken long ago. The person is dead, yet there lies still his body, perhaps panting for breath, gurgling in the throat, passing water into the sheets. Limbs may twitch and there is the indescribable odour of the chamber of death in a small room of an ancient building. The district nurse calls as often as she can, and so does the doctor. In the end the relatives can be quite beside themselves with the burden of nursing someone dearly loved, but who has long since departed, so that they have only this travesty of an animated corpse left in the bedroom.

Legislation on voluntary euthanasia could never settle the issue in this case; indeed it would hopelessly complicate and delay it. I am fully satisfied, speaking as a common man, on the basis of our common humanity, that on rare occasions, in these cases, there comes a time when the nurse asks, 'Why change the sheets again, for the second time this evening? He may get a bedsore, but he will almost certainly die first.' And the wife says 'Why go on trying to get these motionless lips to swallow the tea that has been vomited up three times already? He has gone away already – he is not here. He is not thirsty any more; I am putting down the feeding cup and will just go on holding the hand of him who was once the person so dear to me.'

Then, occasionally, but in my experience rarely, a good doctor with the full knowledge of the nurse and the approval of the spouse, decides that everyone, including the patient, should have a good night's rest, come what may. I have known occasions when a very large dose of a sedative has given everyone twelve hours of solid sleep and the patient has had a reasonable night and is still alive, even more vigorous, twenty-four hours later, and needs another sedative. I have also known other occasions when stupor and sleep deepened into death, but no one could tell how much it was the large dose of sedative, how much it was the disease and its complications, and how much it was the lack of food and drink that allowed that unconscious body to cease to function. This I am fully satisfied occasionally happens. I regard it as perfectly good medical practice and I am fully satisfied that whatever is the state of the law on the books that no doctor performing his duty and his charity to someone who has ceased to be a person, not only in his own eyes as the medical attendant, but also in the eyes of the nurse, and even more in the eyes of the spouse and the relatives, need fear any police enquiry, any prosecution, or any conviction. This is, in my opinion, a wicked bogey, conjured up by some of the supporters of legislation on voluntary euthanasia. Instead this doctor is esteemed in the sight of all men. He has already been weighed, tested, approved and praised in the judgment of those most deeply concerned, the spouse and the family, the nurse and perchance other doctors who may have been involved.

Justice, charity and skill have been shown forth, in circumstances that are truly exceptional, and which are becoming less frequent in the modern world where more and more people die in hospital. This certainly cannot be called voluntary euthanasia: the person as a thinking, rational person was already dead, he could no longer choose death by euthanasia. It cannot even be called the termination of the life of a person: the person died long ago; one was left with a mindless, poorly functioning body. Even after the body did eventually die, and heart and brain ceased to function, the blood would be still alive; it could be used for a blood transfusion. One cannot say that the person is still alive just because the dead corpse has living blood in it, or that it is murder to move the body until all the blood cells are dead. The hair follicles will go on living for several days after the death certificate has been written, even after the person has been buried. Similarly, occasionally, just occasionally, even before death of heart, lungs and breathing have occurred, doctor and friends can say that the person, as a person, has died and decisions on his behalf must be taken by those who kept faithful covenant with him in life: wife, children, nurse, doctor, solicitor and minister.

Even in hospital, we are faced on very rare occasions with unusual circumstances best left to the care and conscience of competent doctors and nurses doing openly in the sight of all men whatever is best for the patient, as a person with whom they covenanted to keep faith. There are not many such occasions, but they do occur. One example will be given, known from personal experience. In one of the most respected of the London hospitals a child had been operated on for a tumour of the brain; a malignant form of tumour had been found, but proved inoperable. Soon after the operation the child started to develop mental signs and became unconscious, for the brain was being destroyed. Serious repeated fits occurred. The child became noisy and violent, quite unable to speak or to recognize her parents. It was impossible to control the noisy shouting and groans without continuous sedation. This was attempted for several days, but the other children in the ward became frightened on hearing these sounds. The child's body could only be fed through a tube and eventually after a medical consultation it was decided to stop feeding the child. But still the body just would not die; the brain was almost completely dead, but the young heart and lungs were extremely healthy. The parents and staff became worn out tending this shouting mindless animated corpse. Then the senior physician, after asking the parents' full permission, in the presence of the ward sister, and other members of the staff, increased the sedative until the body which had lost mind and soul many days before ceased to scream and twitch. The chaplain had been informed and was present with the parents in the adjoining room. The full dose of the sedative was written on the treatment sheet by the consultant, who signed with his own initials. The parents the day before had given verbal permission for this treatment in the presence of three members of the staff. Everyone felt that the child had ceased to be a person many days before and that they were merely preparing the body for burial. This is not voluntary euthanasia; the child had ceased to be a person who could express any wish many days before. It would not be aided but impeded by legislation on the matter. I wish to repeat that this is a very exceptional case in which an honourable doctor did that which he felt was most in the interests of the dead body.

No one likes this kind of event, and that is right. Indeed it would be a terrible day for the medical profession and for any hospital if this ever became a common event. It is best kept in check by this feeling of abhorrence. This is one of the reasons why in forty years' association with various hospitals I have only heard of two occasions on which this occurred. A doctor knows that a malicious relative or nurse could perhaps cause serious scandal by noisome rumour in the wrong quarters. This keeps the practice in check and this is right. The occasion must be truly exceptional: the person should be dead as a person in the judgment of the family and all members of the staff, all of whom must signify their approval. This is no argument for voluntary euthanasia; in fact the law on the books keeps this practice to a bare essential minimum, which is the main reason for refusing to tamper with the existing law. It protects against abuse; nothing else can do so.

It is quite common for a medical practitioner to be approached by the spouse or other member of the patient's family with a request that the patient shall not be allowed to suffer agonies, to undergo severe suffering to no purpose, and that nothing should be done to prolong life that is a sheer misery to all concerned. The doctor, realizing how limited are his powers to prolong life, how ineffective are the antibiotics in the terminal stage, can usually completely reassure these anxious relatives. They rarely state bluntly that they want the patient to be killed, and would be horrified at such a suggestion, especially as almost invariably they have never discussed this request with the patient concerned. The relatives have been told the dread diagnosis and the gloomy prognosis, and, little realizing how limited are the powers of the doctor in the terminal stages of incurable illness to prolong life, they take the doctor on one side and beseech him to do nothing to prolong the agony, which is also their agony. They ask very rightly that the patient shall suffer no unnecessary pain, and that his life will not be prolonged by unnecessary medical or surgical interference. They can be completely reassured on both these points.

It is very seldom that the relatives bring it upon themselves to discuss all this with the patient himself. Indeed a large part of the anxiety of relatives in these cases is due to the fact that they usually are quite unable to share all this with the person concerned. He has been kept all too often in complete ignorance of his fate. This is one of the reasons why relatives take the doctor aside and beseech him to do all in his power to mitigate the sufferings.

Suicide as a personal decision to die

In severe progressive illness, especially if it is accompanied by severe pain, I have known several instances where the patient has terminated his own life by taking a large number of sedative tablets. Often a note is left explaining matters and asking that no resuscitation should be attempted. I have never met one of these notes myself, but I have heard of them. If I found such a note by someone who had an incurable complaint, I would respect his wishes, and I think this would be the attitude of the large majority of doctors.

As far as my personal experience goes, I think that most of those who commit suicide because of an incurable complaint have not been able to discuss this step with their relatives. This seems to be a pity, but is perhaps understandable. It therefore usually comes as a great shock to the family and friends. The blow is mitigated by the knowledge that there was an incurable complaint, but there are often regrets that the decision could not have been shared, that the farewell was so abrupt, even furtive. It leaves a sourness in the mouth and a distaste in the memory.

Suicide is however in a sense the only honest method in which to terminate one's life because of some mortal, incurable, painful complaint. In this a man exercises his liberty to end his own life. He has lived with this liberty all his life; now in the light of what he knows about the nature of his illness, the certainty of his fate, the probability of severe pain, or declining powers, or loss of human dignity, a man decides that, on balance, life is not worth living. It is his decision and many would say it is his life. This is where a man's basic outlook on life comes out. From one point of view, it might be said that it was his own life and therefore that he was free to decide whether to live or to end his life. Looking at in another way, one might observe that it is not his life. He did not make his own body, fashion his own mind, make his own personality; he could not say, as the outside agent: I made this, I own this, it is mine. On the biological level he received life from mother and father, they from their parents and they in turn from a stream of ancestors. The individual may have his own genetic code, different from every other person that was, and is and is to be, but every cipher in that code came from some ancestor or other, way out and long back for a thousand and more generations. Perchance he has handed on half of his genes to meet and mingle with an equal number from his mate. These genes meet and mingle in their own dance of love that heralds a new genetic number, a new individual, a new fertilized ovum.

On the human plane a person knows he is not alone. Fate and fortune have joined his life to that of others. So it is a false simplification for a man to speak of 'the life that I have', and to say, 'I can decide, by myself, to terminate my own life'. The hallmark of suicide is that a man must do it alone; he can seldom discuss it with the nearest and dearest. Perchance they will not agree; perhaps they will attempt to resuscitate him. It is most exceptional for anyone who is contemplating suicide to discuss it rationally with his friends. Dark hints may be made, threats can be uttered, a cry for help may be heard, but in forty years of professional life I have never met a suicide who has been able to discuss the matter calmly with a friend, gain his approval and his co-operation. Doubtless, since circumstances and human nature are both so varied there are occasions when a rational human being desires death, takes counsel with kith and kin and wins their approval. This approval is signified by encouraging the suicide to terminate his life in circumstances known to them, and they make no effort to prevent it, or to resuscitate him. All this may happen, but it must be extremely rare.

Occasionally perhaps someone committing suicide makes some one person party to his intention; he can hardly make him a party to the action without involving the risk of a charge of manslaughter, if not murder. Notes may be left exonerating his assistant in the act of suicide, but the main actor will have been removed by death; he can no longer speak in defence of his assistant who may be charged with homicide. Dimly realizing all this, almost all those contemplating suicide, for whatever reason, will take counsel of none, nor ask any man for assistance. The same will be true of any decision to terminate one's own life because of incurable distressing mortal sickness. These people are most unlikely to take counsel of anyone or to ask assistance of their fellow men.

Even if the Suicide Act (1961) were modified in England and Wales so that it ceased to be illegal to assist suicide in someone suffering from severe, incurable, distressing illness, it seems unlikely that this would often occur. Even then, the person who assisted the suicide might be exposed to the charge of homicide, unless it could be proved that assistance had been requested. There is at present no evidence that in Scotland, where it is not an offence to assist suicide, this relaxation has solved the problem posed by incurable, distressing illness. If legislation were introduced in England to cover this contingency, then it would prove necessary to define incurable illness, and one likely to cause severe distress. So we are back again once more at all the difficulties that would attend the certification of severe incurable distressing illness by two doctors, as envisaged in the Voluntary Euthanasia Bill of 1969. Would then a potential suicide have to obtain two certificates in order to exonerate his assistant from the possibility of any criminal charge?

Unless due cause can be shown to modify the existing law, it is best to leave it as it is, and allow any mitigation to proceed from leniency in enforcement. Strange as it may seem, in this deeply human situation of life and death, there seems to be everything to be said for keeping the laws in the books exactly as they are, for they are guardians against abuse and protectors against foul play. If there are any exceptions to these laws, then the common man recognizes them to be exceptions and not precedents. Life seems to demand certain clearcut rules and conventions, which everyone knows and respects. One should drive on one side of the road, assuming that everyone on all occasions will do the same. We can then proceed along the road at speed and in comparative safety. This is not to say that on very rare occasions we may not choose to vary this rule, but only under the most exceptional circumstances, which we may be called upon to

justify in a court of law. Matters will not be improved by legislating
for the exceptions to the Highway Code. In a similar way there is one
rule about life: that no man should take another's life. There is one
rule for medical practice: that a doctor keeps faith with a patient as
the guardian of his life. Exceptions there may be; let them be as few
as possible and answerable always in the courts of the land and
within the conscience of all men.

When all this has been said, the problem posed by legislation on
voluntary euthanasia still stands: too often people linger on in pain
and distress that is hard to bear and loathsome to behold. It has been
submitted that legislation on voluntary euthanasia can never solve
this problem and it has been argued that assistance in suicide would
also prove ineffective. What remains?

Rare occurrences

It is first necessary to consider the last red herring, which is that doctors do occasionally perform euthanasia in an unobtrusive manner,
as a great mercy. My enquiries, for what they are worth, do not support this contention. Undoubtedly there are a good many rumours
and stories to this effect. I am not impressed by these tales. They are
the kind which are told over a round of drinks in a bar, or at the
dinner table. I was regaled quite recently by one vivid account from
an eminently respectable hairdresser, who gave graphic details of a
brother dying in agony; then the doctor gave a final shot and that was
that. It was a good story until he spoiled it by saying that he was one
of five brothers, and that three of them had departed thus, in the
same cathedral city, at the hands of the same doctor, all being nursed
at home, and all dying of cancer. Now cancer is not the commonest
form of death: it is very unlikely that three brothers would die of
cancer, all in the same city and all under the same doctor, all being
nursed at home. I might have believed the single narrative, but not
the embroidered triplet.

Those with experience in geriatric wards and units for terminal
care know how often words spoken to anxious relatives are mis-
interpreted. A doctor is asked by a relative not to let the agony go on
much longer; he gives an assurance that the patient will get a good
sleep this very night. Some injection or pill is given; death occurs
during the night; the relatives are much relieved, nod to one another
and agree to say nothing. But they know, they say, that the doctor
ended the life. Many genuine examples of this misunderstanding have

come to my personal attention, and I have confirmed that it occurs frequently in special units for terminal care.

Another source of misunderstanding arises on the numerous occasions when it is decided to withdraw active medical treatment during the last stages of terminal illness. Thus an elderly person may be slowly dying of heart failure, and requires some regular injection of, say, digitalis to slow the rapid irregular pulse. The time comes when the person is obviously dying and has only a short time to live, and a decision is made to stop all active medical treatment that is not relieving pain. The regular injections of digitalis are stopped; actually at this stage they are almost useless. Death occurs a few hours later. The doctors attribute this to progressive heart failure, but relatives may speak about the decision to stop useless treatment as terminating the life of the person; they may call it euthanasia. The doctor, they say, stopped the injections that they had regarded as indispensable to life. This is not correct; they had become quite ineffective in a dying person. Digitalis does not work if the heart is near to death, so why continue the useless injection?

Another frequent source of misunderstanding arises over the use of sedatives, a misunderstanding not confined to the relatives; it may even arise in the mind of the nurses, and is often present in the mental background of the doctor. Thus suppose a person is dying from an advanced cancer and has had a fair amount of pain. At first this would be well controlled by tablets, later on injections of a narcotic drug would be started, eventually the dose would be increased, and this would occur more than once. Eventually as the end approaches, some doctors may feel that it is so important to offer more relief at night, and for the relatives to know that this will occur, that they may increase the dose yet once more, but only slightly so. If the patient dies the first time that the dose is raised, then human nature being what it is, many a junior doctor will have scruples, he will fear that the dose proved too much. He may even be so unwise as to say this to the nursing staff. The relatives may be much relieved and may thank the nursing staff for ensuring that relief was given; the nurse may reply somewhat cryptically that, after all, 'It was for the best.' Nothing more is said, but the relatives are certain that an injection sufficiently large to ensure death was deliberately planned and administered. Nothing could be further from the truth.

As far as I can ascertain, and I have spoken to many doctors about this, it is extremely rare for a conscious rational patient to ask deliberately for death at the hands of his doctor, and for the doctor to agree to terminate his life days or weeks before death would naturally have occurred. This is voluntary euthanasia, the matter that is under debate, the situation for which some consider that legislation is required. Persistent enquiry concerning this type of case suggests that this occurrence is extremely rare.

It is a different matter when death is very near to hand and its arrival is manifest to all, for a person to express a desire to die. Indeed that is right and natural, it represents the patient's acceptance of death. Many must feel thus, even if they seldom bring themselves to voice the secrets of their hearts. At first the idea may present itself as a great fear, with which a man must contend as with a mortal foe. Later the adversary may be tolerated, even accepted. Finally shortly before death the prospect is welcomed. Such is the lot of most men confronted in the prime of life with the face of death. The elderly and the infirm have come often to accept death in a most natural manner. They speak of their decease in a disconcerting, matter-of-fact way; often they think of it in terms of meeting again those who have gone before. They may come to desire death and speak about it openly. This again is right and natural, however much it disturbs those who visit them. In an even flat voice they announce in a matter-of-fact manner that they want to die. This indeed is a trump card to which there is no reply. I am firmly convinced that in the large majority of cases these elderly persons do not want to have life terminated. If one of the disconcerted visitors produced a few tablets and said, 'Take these: they will send you to sleep and you will never wake again; isn't that what you want?', the tablets would seldom be taken. If the tablets were left by the bedside, they would be there next morning. Indeed, if they had disappeared and the patient had departed one would be left with the haunting fear that they had been swallowed only in a mental muddle, which is such a common feature in a person of declining powers. Had they dozed off early in the evening and woken, seen some tablets, taken a couple, dozed off, woken still more muddled and settled for the balance, one by one, as a mechanical, drugged automaton? Things like this have happened many times with elderly persons.

Whichever way we look at this problem, it does not appear that legislation will solve the issue, or indeed will aid the solution. There are many problems which cannot be solved by legislation. Those who choose to exercise their liberty to die ought to do so by acting as their own arbiter, as at present, playing their part as a man, not delegating decisions to a medical tribunal, not pushing their indecision on to others. Perhaps some of them will lay by a store of tablets against a rainy day. Anyone who is firmly of this opinion should treat the matter in this cold and calculated manner. They could even deposit them in the security of their bank, and give instructions for them to be sent, should occasion arise. If this procedure was not encouraged by the banks, following a few publicized cases of euthanasia, it must be asked whether some public-minded body should not ask people to register with them, pay a small fee, buy some lethal tablets, address the package to themselves, then leave everything in the central office until they sent accredited instructions for their despatch by recorded delivery. Should some body, called possibly Suicides Synonymous, be set up, even endowed by former recipients?

Death is not robbed of its sting by stupid quips. Those who support voluntary euthanasia have a strong case: there is a problem here, even if it will never be solved, but only vexed beyond reason by legislation. It will only be mitigated by recognition. At present it suffers far too much by neglect. Too many are frankly hypocritical and say that there is no problem here; then they are admitted as a spectator to a private box and death is on the stage, at their elbow, and the chief actor is a loved one, bowed out under a burden of flowers and tears. They are appalled, even bitter; they never dreamed that death could be so devastating. They thought that death was merely falling asleep; alas, they are completely shaken.

Increased recognition of the problem by the medical profession

Much has to be done by the medical profession. I can only record to my shame that although I taught medicine to medical students for about twenty-five years, I never remember that I did anything at all to help them to understand the human issues that are involved in dying. Perhaps I did something in my attitudes, I hope so; but this is not enough. Granted that the medical students are not mature in their profession, but at least they can watch what one does. In my own student days at St Thomas's in the 1920s, the consultants seldom seemed to have time to discuss matters with the patients and their relatives. Having said this, I wonder whether my medical students, when I taught medicine in East Africa, often saw me stay to discuss matters with the patient or his family.

Doctors must face up to this problem far more than has occurred in the past. The increase in the modern methods of resuscitation only intensify the problem. As every new method is produced it must be tried on all manner of cases, it cannot be offered exclusively to young persons. Within the past few decades it has been demonstrated, for instance that even elderly persons can often benefit by operations, which would not have been contemplated years ago. People over eighty years of age, who are in constant pain from osteo-arthrosis (arthritis) of the hip, and unable to stand for any length of time because of severe pain, can be transformed by a modern operation to restore the hip joint. The arthritis would never have killed them; modern surgery often transforms their lives. In a similar manner, elderly diabetics are now treated with insulin, although in 1946 a doctor on the Isle of Wight consulted with me whether to treat my father, aged 72, for his diabetes and decided that at his age this was not desirable. Had it been possible to give him insulin, as it would today, he would have lived to achieve the great ambition of his life: it would have proved possible for him to travel in the congested post-war transport to stay with his only daughter, a doctor, married and with her husband and family waiting for him in Australia. I shall always keep, just as a reminder, his last note to me, in which he stated his unfulfilled wish, lest we talk too glibly of keeping useless old folk alive with unnecessary medical treatment.

It is impossible to keep long-stay incurable patients in any number in a modern teaching hospital, and the respected heads of the medical profession seldom see this kind of patient, at least for any length of time. Medical students too are naturally concerned with curative medicine and surgery, they are seldom attracted towards any consideration of the treatment of incurable illness. Only those of a mature temperament can see that all this is a real part of the practice of medicine. Most doctors pick up in a desultory and unsystematic manner the skills involved in the medical care of those slowly dying of an incurable and painful illness. The doctor feels committed to them as patients and as persons with whom he keeps faith, even when their deterioration mocks his clinical skill. The knowledge of the correct use of drugs is not easy to pick up in a desultory manner, and this may explain why some doctors still exhibit only a modicum of skill. There is great need for all medical students as a part of their medical training to visit units of terminal care. There is also great necessity to increase facilities for special short courses of instruction at these units, when all aspects can be fully discussed with practitioners anxious to increase their skill, not only with modern drugs, but in the psychological, social and personal aspects of good care of those dying from incurable, progressive illness, especially if it is accompanied by severe pain and considerable disability.

Great credit is due to those who have emphasized for a long time that this has tended to be one of those neglected areas of modern medicine. At present there are only two hundred consultant geriatricians in Britain; as the number increases, this branch of medicine will improve. Geriatric units have revolutionized the approach in many parts of the country, but I know from personal experience other parts of the land where facilities are poor. There may have been for many years no senior appointments in nursing, in medical care, or in geriatric skills. These are all needed if this problem is to receive the attention that it requires. It is marvellous what has been done, in spite of the shortage of money. It pained me as a vicar to visit the elderly folk of the parish in one institution, a modified Victorian workhouse, striving to do its best under impossible conditions, where the dead hand of public finance flattened the face of everything.

The only thing which will keep the problem of euthanasia alive, past the corrosions of time, will be the eternal, unsolved, problem that will abide with us till time is no more: people who are persons in their own right, dying, with powers of body and mind diminishing, always with some measure of distress, at least mental distress, often with some disability, always with much weakness, usually with some pain, dying and knowing usually that they are dying, going away, leaving those they love and places that they have known. To the end of time let us hope this calls out human sympathy and human devotion: without these, all other provision, be it never so costly in money, so marvellous in its scientific design, is a mere nothing. Those who have escaped from a great fire can return to teach us how to be wise; those who have escaped drowning can return to insist on better safety precautions, even endow lifeboats, but those who are dying can never, never return to teach us how we should have done it better. This, like so many problems concerning death, is built into the situation, unaltered by any discovery of science, uninfluenced by any legislation of parliament. Those who think we can escape by some voluntary choice on our own part, are deluding themselves into the belief that death is like any other situation in life. It is completely different.

Death is death. I have watched it in the face of the aged African peasant, dying in his mud hut, to be buried soon in the tilth of the banana groves; he knows in a deep sense that he is going home to his fathers. As the scene darkens and the senses fail, I have marvelled at the quiet spirituality, the naturalness of it all: acceptance, peace at the last, going home, the human spirit rising above all its temporalities and trivialities, facing the eternal verities. I have watched it as an African mother weeps and wails over the dead body of her malnourished child, dying of the nameless disease that we never understood until a mere yesterday, and concerning which, if I need any epitaph, let it be 'He wrote the first book on kwashiorkor, the disease of the world's poor malnourished children.' I have seen death in the hospital beds of the English hospital, where I stood hopeless, helpless and dumb, as the chaplain, while everyone else was doing something useful. I stood for the relatives, who feel they can do nothing but stand and wait. That is a part of our human lot, that we are almost helpless and hopeless in the face of death. We must all stand in the shadow of this cross.

Yet I have learned that there is another side to the picture, for as the strength ebbs from the faces and spirit of the helpless relatives, so it seems to deepen and strengthen in the spirit of the patient. That is the eternal miracle about so many dying persons, particularly those who are not too much marred by disease or muddled by sedatives or weakened by age.

Dying and death can only be transformed, and its dolours mitigated, by those who have thought out their position with regard to death. It is the unthinking man who cannot face the dark night. In the modern world Western man, adrift from his moorings, projects his fears and uncertainties on to the question of death. It has become and it will probably remain a taboo subject, to which however he is existentially linked. It will end all his hopes: he will meet it one day, come what may.

This situation needs to be transformed; it has to be redeemed. This is what the Gospel is all about: it is quite literally Good News. It is received like all the good things of life, like the act of love, like birth, death and eternal life, in faith and trust, like a child, who is beginning to know, however slightly and inadequately, the one who is Father, the one who is God. He gave life to us, when there was no life; to him we yield our lives in death to be held safe and secure. As the arms of the nurses lift us on to the last journey, we trust that underneath are in very truth the Everlasting Arms.

APPENDIX A

The Problem of Euthanasia

*A Report prepared by a Special Panel appointed by the
Board of Science and Education of the British Medical Association*

January 1971

Introduction

The word euthanasia means literally 'a good death' or 'gentle easy death'
but the term is rarely used in this sense at the present time. Euthanasia has
now come to mean the deliberate termination of the life of a person who is
suffering from a distressing irremediable disease. Voluntary euthanasia
implies that an adult person of sane mind has expressed an informed wish
for euthanasia. Much confusion can be avoided if the terms euthanasia and
voluntary euthanasia are taken in this, as opposed to the literal, sense. But
it must be emphasized that euthanasia means killing.

Many of the arguments about euthanasia rest upon misunderstandings.
There should be no misunderstanding in the minds of doctors about their
duties towards their dying patients; certainly there is widespread misunderstanding among the public about the position of doctors and nurses in this
matter. The general purpose of this paper is to attempt to remove some of
the current confusion of thought.

Death

Peaceful Dying The general public commonly supposes that dying is
inevitably a difficult and distressing process. The fact that the majority of
deaths are peaceful, whatever the preceding illness, needs greater emphasis.
Contrary to popularly held opinion, even the majority of patients suffering
from cancer die peacefully. It is in the preceding stages of terminal illness
that relief of pain and distress is needed. Some of the emotion behind the
demand for euthanasia lies in the belief that death will be peaceful and
dignified only after a lethal injection.

Expectations of the Dying Patient The experience of those who look after
the dying is that patients seldom ask to die and rarely to be killed. Many of
them do not seem to realize that they are dying and even when they do,
they still welcome any prolongation of life, especially if this can be gained

with comfort and dignity and they can see their friends. They trust their doctors and nurses; they would not expect to give directions about the management of their last days, still less would they wish to determine their end.

Legal Position

The Present Position   Under existing law it is illegal to terminate the life of anyone deliberately. The doctor is in no way different from an ordinary subject of the realm as regards his right to kill a dying patient. Some people think that under certain circumstances doctors should be permitted by law to end the life of a patient suffering from an incurable disease and who wishes to die; with this in mind, the Voluntary Euthanasia Bill was introduced in 1969.

Suicide   Those who wish to change the law emphasize that since 1961 it is no longer a crime to attempt to commit suicide. The Suicide Act, however, is not intended to signify social approval of suicide. Its real purpose is to ensure that those who fail in their suicide attempt should be recognized as patients requiring treatment and should not be punished as law breakers. The Act contains penalties of up to fourteen years imprisonment for those who aid suicide because it is felt that suicide should be discouraged. Few events distress a family so deeply as suicide; euthanasia is akin to suicide and would also be distressing.

Do Doctors Already Perform Euthanasia?   There are people who believe that some doctors deliberately kill incurable patients by administering a lethal dose of a drug. The view of the panel is that if this does occur it is confined to the very few and cannot be condoned. Most doctors see no need for new legislation to protect them when discharging their normal duty towards their dying patients.

Medical Problems

Relief of Pain   For those who are dying from painful conditions, doctors can and do provide relief by means of analgesic drugs. In order to relieve pain during a terminal illness it is sometimes necessary to increase gradually the dose of drugs. The main consideration is to ensure that such drugs are administered in doses adequate to alleviate pain. Regular increases in doses may be necessary because the disease becomes more severe or because the patient acquires tolerance to the drug. The risk of respiratory depression may occur with rather higher doses than are needed purely for the relief of pain (the amount varying from drug to drug). It is possible to give opiates to ease pain for many weeks or months, without killing the patient. Newer drugs may increase the margin of safety but the skilful use of older remedies can still provide satisfactory treatment. Sleep and freedom from pain can be achieved by modern therapeutic measures.

The extent to which relief of pain is available to a sufferer varies according to circumstances. In some instances long periods of heavy sedation resulting in stupor or obliteration of consciousness may be justified; these may be interrupted by periods of consciousness and relief from pain and distress.

Control of pain and alleviation of distress must be the object and not termination of life. Pain is relieved in other ways – by reassurance and by confidence and by rest. Doctors are assisted in this by nurses, by the professions ancillary to medicine and by ministers of religion. The sympathy and support of relatives and friends is also extremely valuable.

Terminal Illness   When a doctor is treating a patient during the last stages of illness and death is inevitable, an intercurrent infection may arise. The relevant treatment then can only be to relieve distress. It is a matter of clinical judgment whether measures such as blood transfusions or use of antibiotics, are correct in the circumstances.

At the sedated terminal stage of illness any need for euthanasia has passed, as care by doctors and nurses has ensured the quiet gentle death desired by the advocates of euthanasia; where the terminal stage is prolonged relatives may become distressed but the welfare of the patient must be the over-riding consideration.

Determination of Death   Many factors are involved in the death of the individual, and the final decision concerning death must be a clinical one. The length of independent survival of the separate tissue systems varies considerably. For example, it is possible artificially to keep heart and lungs functioning alone for a limited period by using a mechanical respirator long after other systems have died. Switching off the respirator in these circumstances after life has been judged extinct clinically is not euthanasia.

Mental Illness   Mental illness may lead to a desire for death at any age. A wish to die should always arouse suspicion of a mental illness such as depression, confusion or paranoia, which can be common reasons for suicide. Mental illness may occur without physical illness or it may arise as a result of physical illness. Modern methods of treatment ensure that many patients recover from mental illness. It would be tragic if a death wish expressed during a temporary state of depression led to euthanasia. Indeed it might be argued that if euthanasia legislation were enacted it would be necessary for every applicant for voluntary euthanasia to be declared as being of sound mind particularly at the time the wish was expressed.

The Elderly   It should be clearly recognized that most elderly patients have come to regard death as an inevitable and natural event and they face the prospect with serenity. Some elderly people, however, feel they have outlived all their usefulness and are a burden to others and hope that death will not be long delayed. In this group there is often a fear that life will be unduly prolonged by modern medical developments without the patient having any choice in the matter. The majority would not make any deliberate attempt to hasten death but there is no doubt that some may desire it, especially if denied the support of relatives and friends. What is needed here is not a change in the law but a change in attitude of people towards their dying elderly relatives and friends.

The argument that the elderly are 'kept alive by the use of drugs' has been grossly exaggerated. There is much evidence to show that even the most potent remedies may become relatively ineffective in old age. Old people are kept alive by kindness, good nutrition and good nursing.

Elderly people are liable to varying degrees of mental impairment and are sometimes referred to by the public as being 'senile' or 'demented'. Their alertness may fluctuate from day to day and is particularly likely to be diminished by toxic complications of illness. At such time they could not be expected to understand the issues involved in euthanasia.

It has been advocated that an adult might sign an application for euthanasia to be undertaken automatically if and when he suffered serious mental impairment at a future date. Life might then be terminated on the patient's previously expressed consent when a degree of dementia was present. Since there is no clear dividing line between the gradually failing mental powers of a rational elderly person and the severe reduction of mental powers in dementia it would be a matter of opinion whether the condition had become established as a permanent state or was in a temporary phase. Euthanasia, a decision to kill, in such circumstances would place an intolerable burden upon the doctor. Nor would the patient be in a fit state to nullify a decision on euthanasia taken some years previously.

It is natural to desire to die with dignity but in advanced age bodily functions and control, for example of bladder and bowels, may become impaired. Failing mental powers may lessen the patient's own awareness of his plight but his condition may cause much distress to relatives. It would be primarily the distress of the relatives that would be relieved by euthanasia in such instances.

Progressive Nervous Illness and Chronic Disabling Disease In contrast to the gradual deterioration of mental and bodily functions that may characterize advancing age, there is a small group of diseases which occur in middle age leaving the mind unimpaired but affecting the nervous system. Patients with slowly progressive neurological disease constitute one of the most difficult problems confronting doctors and nurses, and these diseases place a heavy burden on patients and their relatives. Such patients could have qualified for euthanasia under the terms of the Voluntary Euthanasia Bill. There are other diseases which also cause physical distress and disability and which are more common; such patients, too, could have qualified under the terms of the Bill. These groups of patients will be helped by further research and development so that it will be possible to assist them long before they reach the terminal stage. Advances in medicine are taking place all the time and diseases which have no remedy one year may have effective treatment the next.

Inadequate Facilities Our community has devoted too little of its resources to the care of the elderly and chronic sick. Moreover, it is far easier to obtain publicity and money for spectacular new procedures than it is to provide funds to study the control of severe pain and disability in chronic, progressive and terminal illness. The solution to this problem is to provide more money for better facilities and for research into the relief of distress and disability. Specialized work has shown what can be achieved in this field.

Medical Education

Some medical schools could be criticized in that there has been too little teaching about common conditions. Much is taught about birth and its hazards but at present there seems to be little teaching about what has been aptly called 'perimortal morbidity'. We believe that the problems of death and euthanasia, just as much as those of birth and abortion, should command the attention of teachers and students alike.

Where relief of pain during terminal illness has not been satisfactory it may well be due to insufficient instruction in such matter given to the doctors during their medical training. Teaching and teaching methods are being extended all the time and there are signs that students are very much more keen to learn about care of the dying. Improvements in teaching and a change of emphasis and in attitudes are needed rather than a change in the law. A change in the law would hamper changes in attitudes.

Dangers of Euthanasia Legislation

After careful consideration the panel is convinced that it would be impossible to provide adequate safeguards in any euthanasia legislation.

Errors in Medical Diagnosis and Prognosis Medical diagnosis, even though carefully made and supported by many tests, will always contain an element of fallibility. A recommendation for euthanasia would have to be based upon a diagnosis of irreversible physical or mental disease. Mistakes would inevitably be made.

Prognosis is open to the same errors as diagnosis; it is impossible to be absolutely certain what the future outcome of an illness will be. For these reasons, irreversible mistakes could be made whenever euthanasia was practised.

It will be objected that no human act is free from error and to suspend judgment on that account would imply that any responsible clinical decision should be evaded. But a clinical decision is intended for the benefit of the patient; could a decision to carry out euthanasia be so regarded?

Errors of judgment in curative medicine are inevitable but the majority of these may be and are corrected. Errors of judgment would occur in the identification of the medical conditions deemed to be present and thought to justify euthanasia. Such errors could not be remedied.

Errors in Assessing Terminal Stages of Illness It has been suggested that euthanasia should be restricted to the terminal stages of physical illness. It is not possible to define terminal illness precisely. It must always be a clinical decision when to regard death as imminent. Even at this stage some patients make unexpected recovery.

Errors in the Validity of a Request for Euthanasia Clearly, a request for euthanasia would have to be made freely by a person who understood the nature of his request, and who was not affected by mental illness or by the mistaken impression that he ought to agree to euthanasia in order to spare the time, money, patience and suffering of others. A patient's decision, whether made prior to an illness or during periods of intense suffering, would rely on subjective assessment of the situation and would, therefore, be suspect. As already discussed (p. 153) an expressed desire for death may be a sign of a mental illness, which would render invalid an application for euthanasia.

Medical and Nursing Professions

The confidence which a patient places in his doctors and nurses is to him paramount. This relationship would be placed in jeopardy if the roles of the doctor and nurse were extended to include the task of ending life.

The medical profession of this country has expressed itself strongly in the following resolution of the Representative Body of the British Medical Association of 1969:

RESOLVED: That this Meeting in affirming the fundamental objects of the medical profession as the relief of suffering and the preservation of life, strongly supports Council's view on the condemnation of euthanasia and instructs Council to give this view full publicity.

This opinion was first expressed by the Council in 1950 when it agreed with a pronouncement on these lines by the World Medical Association. The practice of euthanasia was believed to be contrary to the public interest, to medical ethical principles, as well as to natural and civil rights, and contrary to the spirit of the Declaration of Geneva, and the World Medical Association recommended to national medical associations that 'they condemn the practice of euthanasia under any circumstances'.

Those who support euthanasia have always assumed that doctors will both assess the patient's need for it and undertake the task. The decision whether or not to adopt euthanasia would be made, primarily, by society but society could not expect the medical profession to carry it out. To be a trusted physician is one thing; to appear as a potential executioner is quite another. If patients, particularly the elderly and those with cancer phobia, believed that doctors would play an active part in euthanasia some would fear their doctors and possibly avoid them, thereby failing to obtain essential and curative treatment.

Doctors and patients would have cause to be fearful, whatever the safeguards in any euthanasia bill. Pressure might be put upon doctors by relatives of patients to carry out this abhorrent procedure. This is no phantom fear. Such pressure by friends and relations is already familiar to doctors in connection with certificates of incapacity for work and unjustifiable requests for an abortion to be arranged. It might become difficult to control euthanasia.

The nursing profession has always been held in the highest position of trust. Under the Voluntary Euthanasia Bill (1969) it was proposed that a nurse, acting under the instructions of a physician who had made the decision, could administer euthanasia. The strongest possible objections must be lodged against this involvement of the nursing profession.

The tradition of medicine is to cure, to heal and to relieve suffering; to serve as executioner involves a fundamental change of role for the doctor and the nurse. A law to permit euthanasia might damage the vocational aspect of the work and indirectly affect recruitment to the professions.

Other Possible Effects of Euthanasia Legislation

Apart from the general fears that euthanasia legislation would arouse, there are other possible effects to be considered. Relatives often have to bear responsibility for continuing care in terminal illness. If they were to feel that the responsibility for the life-or-death decision rested with them the distress of bereavement might be greatly increased. Bereavement is frequently accompanied by feelings of guilt which may or may not be justified. It would be wrong to add to this grief an intolerable doubt about the rightness of a decision to end the life of one of close kin.

Were euthanasia to become lawful there would be no way of preventing the burden of decision from falling on many who would never have wished to bear it. Such decisions cannot be purely personal but will always involve others.

Proposed euthanasia legislation has excluded those under the age of majority but it might be eventually extended to include children. The burden of decision borne by parents would then be great. Eventually it might be suggested that the law should also cover the destruction of infants suffering from gross deformity or mental deficiency.

Final Considerations

There is a feeling, promoted by the Euthanasia Society, that a person has a 'right to die'. Religious attitudes and legal practice have been built on a fundamentally different principle: 'the right to live'. The ethic of the right to live derives partly from Canon and Roman Law. It was also found in the Hippocratic Oath in the pre-Christian era, and has in recent years been re-affirmed in the Nuremberg Code, subscribed to by the majority of nations, races and creeds of the world, and in the European Convention of Human Rights. Any concession which makes a breach in this principle is dangerous and raises new problems.

One of these problems is in relation to suicide. If the law ever recognized the 'right to die' the medical profession would be exercised to know its position in regard to resuscitation of persons who had attempted to commit suicide, a common medical emergency. At present the position is clear; doctors and nurses do their utmost to preserve life. In the majority of instances the patient survives; a minority regret their resuscitation and make a second attempt. If the law were changed, would the unsuccessful suicide be in a position to prosecute the doctors and nurses who had interfered with this newly proposed basic right – 'the right to die'?

Clearly, euthanasia legislation would be a licence for the killing of human beings. It seems an anachronism to introduce it at a time when capital punishment has been abolished and the young are openly moving towards pacifism. The memory of what occurred under the Nazis where euthanasia was practised to 'improve the race' cannot be dismissed. Civilizations are sometimes judged by their care of the poor, the weak, the elderly and the infirm. In the past societies may have been justified in exposing the weaker members of the tribe to adversity with lethal intent. But neither eugenic nor personal reasons can justify the extermination of dependent members of an advanced society.

Euthanasia cannot be accepted by the medical profession; in rejecting it doctors will be supported by the majority of laymen who share the belief that the deliberate killing of a helpless person can never be condoned. It is right that dying patients should be relieved of suffering and this can and should be done. Killing patients is no part of the work of doctors and nurses.

THE MEMBERS OF THE PANEL

The membership of the special panel appointed by the Board of Science and Education, was as follows:

Rev. Dr H. C. Trowell (Chairman), late consultant physician Uganda Medical Department; hospital chaplain, Salisbury General Hospital 1960–69.

Dr J. G. Frost, general practitioner

Dr Ronald Gibson, general practitioner; Chairman B.M.A. Council

Dr R. M. Mayon-White, consultant paediatrician

Dr Cicely Saunders, medical director, St Christopher's Hospice

Professor Sir Ronald Tunbridge, Professor of Medicine and consultant physician; Chairman, B.M.A. Board of Science and Education

Dr Duncan Vere, consultant physician

Dr Christina Williams, senior registrar in geriatrics

Dame Albertine Winner, deputy medical director, St Christopher's Hospice

Secretariat: Dr Walter Hedgcock, Secretary of the Board of Science and Education of the B.M.A., and Miss I. M. Marriage, S.R.N.

The Panel has consulted whomsoever it has thought appropriate including a number of the younger members of the medical profession, and representatives of the Euthanasia Society both lay and medical.

Doctors and Euthanasia

A rejoinder to the British Medical Association's report
'The Problem of Euthanasia'

The Voluntary Euthanasia Society, May 1971

Introduction

The introduction to the BMA pamphlet states that its general purpose is to attempt to remove some of the current confusion of thought. Many of the arguments about euthanasia, it is alleged, rest on misunderstandings.

There is certainly no misunderstanding on the part of those responsible for the policy of the Voluntary Euthanasia Society which was founded by doctors and churchmen deeply disturbed about the prolonged pain and distress suffered by some incurable and dying patients. The Society has doctors on its Executive Committee, and its booklet *A Plea for Voluntary Euthanasia* is sponsored by eminent members of the medical and legal professions. On the ethical side, it has the support of prominent churchmen.

What 'misunderstandings' there may be in the public mind have largely been created by the misrepresentation of opponents who would deny freedom of choice to the individual. Allegations are frequently made that the Society aims 'to do away with old and handicapped people, with deformed children and mental defectives' but these could never honestly be made by anyone who has read the Society's literature or any of the Voluntary Euthanasia Bills presented to Parliament.

The major advances in medicine, science, surgery, biology and geriatrics have created tremendous medical and ethical problems. As a doctor put it in the *British Medical Journal* (August 1969): 'Medical progress is keeping alive, or rather "preventing from dying", many for whom life holds out no prospects of a worthwhile existence, and large numbers have reached an age and condition in which their only prospect is mental or physical suffering.' It is this prospect and not the inevitability of death itself which justifiably creates anxiety.

There are growing demands for new, hard thinking on this vital subject but, as the Editor of the London Medical Group's *Matters of Life and Death* (1970) says: 'The time has passed when either the medical profession itself or the Church or the Law could act in isolation on these matters.'

He emphasized that 'what is required is that the different disciplines should learn to listen to each other and thence to evaluate and apply the available insights. Uncritical acceptance by one profession of the statements of the representatives of another may be worse than useless.'

It is in this context that the BMA Report should be evaluated.

Terms of Reference of the Panel

This was not an enquiry conducted in a judicial spirit. The panel was bound by the Resolution passed by the BMA Representative Body in 1969:

> That this Meeting in affirming the fundamental objects of the medical profession as the relief of suffering and the preservation of life, strongly supports the Council's view on the condemnation of euthanasia and instructs Council to give this view full publicity.

The relief of suffering and the preservation of life are commendable objects but they are useless when they conflict, which is precisely when euthanasia becomes relevant.

The panel was bound by this resolution and it was their task to find supporting arguments for it. The fact that they were so bound meant that nobody who disagreed could possibly have served on the panel, which consisted solely of convinced supporters of this Resolution. Their conclusions were decided in principle, though not in detail, before they ever began to sit. It is noteworthy that there is no minority report, something that would have been expected in such a contentious matter if there had been any open-mindedness.

The panel does not seem to have taken any evidence from outside bodies other than the Voluntary Euthanasia Society; at least there is no mention of any other witnesses. This cannot be regarded as a responsible way to examine such life and death issues.

There is no bibliography; and it does not appear from the text that the panel spent any time in reading the large amount of literature on the subject (e.g. the well-known work of Professor John Hinton).

One is struck by the fact that there has been no consideration of fundamental issues. Throughout, death is taken to be an unmitigated evil, when this is far from being a realistic view such as one would expect from doctors. For the dying man, death is an unqualified boon; it is not humane medical practice to struggle against an approaching and inevitable death.

Similarly, life is taken to be, in all circumstances whatever, something good and desirable, even when, say, it is the vegetative existence of the mindless patient in a psychogeriatric ward.

Finally, there is an implicit but absolute denial of the patient's rights of self-determination. It is, it seems, for the doctor to say how long he is to be kept alive, even when he is, perhaps, longing to die. Other symptoms of this attitude are shown in references to suicide.

There is repeated evidence of emotional bias, not only in the nature of the arguments employed but also in the emotive language – 'abhorrent procedure' and 'to serve as executioner'.

The report fails to emphasize, as it should have at the outset, that voluntary euthanasia would involve only those doctors willing to be involved. Also, as the Chairman of the Central Committee for Hospital Medical Services said at the BMA Council Meeting on 5 December 1970 when the Report was under consideration, the profession appeared to be setting itself up to make comments on the wisdom or otherwise of voluntary euthanasia whereas whether it was adopted or not was a decision which society would make.

Comments on the BMA Report

Peaceful Dying It may well be that the majority of deaths are peaceful but no one can deny that a minority are *not*. Neither can it be denied that in some cases of terminal malignant disease modern drugs cannot ensure that dying patients do not unduly suffer. One BMA doctor admitted to 5% but other experts put it at 7% to 13%. Whatever the figure, it is far too large and must represent a tremendous amount of pain and distress.

In these circumstances the doctor has to choose between the preservation of life and the relief of suffering. He cannot have both. If the patient's life is preserved he will suffer: if his suffering is relieved he will die. In such a situation the wishes of the patient should surely be respected. Moreover, a signed and witnessed declaration of a patient's wishes would, in the opinion of some doctors, be very helpful to them when faced with such a vital decision. (The Voluntary Euthanasia Society has a printed form for this purpose.)[1]

The Report says that some of the emotion behind the demand for euthanasia lies in the belief that death will be peaceful and dignified only after a lethal injection. This is certainly not the belief of the Voluntary Euthanasia Society. Most deaths may be peaceful, but it is the preceding stages of terminal illness about which there is growing concern. These stages are part of the process of dying, and they may go on for weeks and months and even, in the case of the senile dement for instance, for years.

Expectations of the Dying Patient The Report contends that dying patients 'seldom ask to die and rarely to be killed'. As the majority of deaths are peaceful, naturally no such request would be expected in these circumstances, but voluntary euthanasia is concerned with that unfortunate minority whose suffering cannot be relieved. But is it true that these unfortunate people seldom ask to die and rarely to be killed? In two combined National Opinion Polls, each of 1,000 General Practitioners taken in 1964 and 1965 at random from the Medical Register, 48·6% of those who replied answered 'Yes' to the question: 'Have you ever been asked by a dying patient to give him or her final release from suffering which was felt to be intolerable?'

It is not unreasonable to suggest that many would refrain from making such a request because, as the law now stands, they would not dare to ask their doctor – such an authoritative, respected and even feared figure – for something they know is illegal and something which they feel he would scornfully reject or even, perhaps, regard as an insult to his professional

[1] See Appendix D.

ego. If the legal option of voluntary euthanasia were open, more patients would feel free to talk to their doctors and make their wishes known.

It is difficult to imagine what evidence the panel has for the statement that 'patients who know they are dying still welcome any prolongation of life'. It must be extremely difficult, if not impossible, to know what is going on in the mind of dying patients, even for those who look after them. Some may wish to lay down the burden of life and others may wish to cling on to it: everything would depend on individual circumstances and attitudes. It is very questionable whether a dying patient who has endured prolonged suffering and distress would welcome any prolongation of life, but if he did, the legalization of voluntary euthanasia would not affect him in any way. He simply would not ask for it. The Voluntary Euthanasia Society has ample evidence that some would prefer an end of their suffering to any prolongation of 'life'.

It is presumptuous for the BMA panel to say that dying persons would not wish to determine their end. Many of us give directions about what is to be done with our bodies after death. Most educated, intelligent people would very much welcome the opportunity of giving directions about the management of their last days, if they were given the chance. Here, as elsewhere in the Report, we see the prevailing medical belief that the patient's body is under the doctor's sole control subject only to a veto, e.g. refusal of an operation, but to no other direction.

Do Doctors Already Perform Euthanasia?   The answer is that some undoubtedly do and this is freely admitted by many doctors. A general practitioner (quoted in the *Birmingham Post*, 21 February 1971) said that in a very few cases 'I have deliberately taken a step to see that someone has taken a dose of a drug which I am well satisfied he will never wake up from'. He is by no means alone. In 'the last stages of illness when death is inevitable', who would criticize a doctor who felt it his duty to shorten useless and prolonged suffering? The assurance so often repeated 'that doctors do not allow dying patients to suffer' is one main reason for the trust which patients have in their doctors. That trust is based on the belief that when inevitable death is accompanied by suffering and distress, the doctor will bring about a peaceful end.

Doctors who take this humane and courageous action are, however, placing themselves at risk with the law, and many must be inhibited from doing so for this reason. Surely this is a cogent argument for the legalization of voluntary euthanasia which would put no obligation on any doctor but would afford him legal protection?

It is, it seems, a standard medical practice to give a patient *in extremis* such a dose of a pain-killing or sedative drug that the doctor faces the *probability* that it will be lethal. Some opponents of voluntary euthanasia contend that there is a great moral difference between this and giving a lethal dose with the certain knowledge that it will end the patient's life. This is a matter of individual conscience, but it is difficult to see any difference in law between giving a drug in the confident expectation, though not certainty, that it will be fatal, and giving a drug known or believed to be lethal.

Relief of Pain Among the victims of cancer, severe and continuous pain is frequently a prominent feature. Sometimes it can be kept within the limit of what is tolerable by the repeated use of narcotics and sedative drugs, but often at the cost of distressing nausea, vomiting and constipation. Sometimes there is deterioration of the personality and other unpleasant side effects. In addition to pain, many victims of cancer have to endure the mental misery associated with the presence of a foul fungating growth; of slow starvation owing to difficulty of swallowing; of painful and frequent micturition; of obstruction of the bowels; of incontinence; of bouts of asphyxia, and of the utter frustration that makes each day and night a 'death in life' as the famous physician, William Osler, described it.

The Report states that the main consideration for those dying from 'painful conditions' is 'to ensure that drugs are administered in doses to alleviate pain'. It is important to note that drugs are to be given to *alleviate* pain and distress, not to obliterate them entirely. The patient is expected to put up with a certain amount of pain and distress, and to go on putting up with them indefinitely. He is, in fact, expected and required to carry on for weeks and months in a state of physical and mental misery which could be obviated by an earlier death.

It is admitted in the Report that 'the extent to which relief of pain is available to a sufferer varies according to circumstances' and it is claimed that 'in some instances long periods of heavy sedation resulting in stupor or obliteration of consciousness may be justified' and that 'these may be interrupted by periods of consciousness and relief from pain and distress'. Many people will find little comfort in such a possibility – to them it would seem like dying several times over.

Except on the grounds of inadequacy, no one would object to the statement that 'Control of pain and alleviation of distress must be the object'. But it is wrong to contrast this with 'the termination of life'. It is a question of how long the suffering has to be endured, and here a patient's wishes should surely be taken into account.

Perhaps the point was best put by a general practitioner (quoted in the *Birmingham Post*, 21 January 1971):

> There comes a time when there is a moribund patient who ought to be dead, and you cannot tell how he manages to go on living, and you give him just a little bit more morphia than he should have, and, thank God, he dies. That is taking on God-like powers, but we do it with humility and love.

Of course the sympathy and support of relatives and friends can often be of great comfort to the dying. But it must be open to question whether this can bring any appreciable relief from pain. Indeed, the patient's knowledge of the distress his prolonged suffering is causing those dear to him is an additional burden he has to bear.

Terminal Illness The BMA are right to say that when a doctor is treating a patient during the last stages of illness and death is inevitable, the welfare of the patient must be the over-riding consideration. But, having recognized that death is inevitable, what is the purpose of such means as blood transfusions or the use of antibiotics? Could the welfare of the patient ever be served by the useless prolongation of dying?

To say, as the BMA Report does, that 'At the sedated terminal stage of illness any need for euthanasia has passed, as care by doctors and nurses has ensured the quiet gentle death desired by the advocates of euthanasia', is to concede that the patient has rightly been drugged into insensibility, as we think he should have been. But this is certainly not always the case. Some doctors, particularly in hospitals, refrain from giving the increasing doses necessary to give total relief from pain as this might hasten death or 'kill the patient'. As a consequence, this gentle death is denied or, more often, unduly delayed.

The Report admits that the terminal stage may be prolonged and that this may distress relatives, and adds, quite rightly, that the welfare of the patient must be the over-riding consideration. But can his welfare ever justify the prolongation of the terminal stage? And is the end to be preceded by long periods of stupor interrupted by periods of consciousness? This is certainly not the gentle, dignified death desired by the advocates of voluntary euthanasia. And it is a strange conception of 'the welfare of the patient'.

Determination of Death   The Report states that 'it is possible artificially to keep heart and lungs functioning alone for a limited period by using a mechanical respirator long after other systems have died', and that to switch off the respirator in these circumstances 'after life has been judged extinct is not euthanasia'. It is surprising that the Panel should have felt it necessary to justify switching off the machine in these circumstances. At this hopeless stage there is no reasonable alternative.

It is the constant reports of unconscious patients being kept alive for weeks or months which give rise to concern. The Report says that 'the final decision concerning death must be a clinical one' but it would seem that what is required is a redefinition of death.

Mental Illness   Mental illness may lead, as the Report says, to a desire for death, and modern treatment may ensure that 'many' patients recover. But it would be quite wrong to assume that a wish for death must necessarily indicate depression, confusion or paranoia. On the contrary, many people in full possession of their mental and physical faculties would regard death as infinitely preferable to an obscene, vegetative existence, mindless, or even worse, conscious of fast diminishing control of mind and body.

The Report is misleading when it warns of the possible tragedy of a death-wish expressed during a temporary state of depression leading to euthanasia. All proposals for the legalization of voluntary euthanasia have provided safeguards against such a possibility. The declaration of a wish for euthanasia in carefully defined circumstances, would be required to be signed by the declarant and two witnesses who testified that its significance was understood, and who would not stand to benefit from the death. The declaration could not come into force until 30 days after being made, and could be revoked at any time. Euthanasia could only be administered when two physicians (one of consultant status) certified that the patient was suffering from an irremediable condition.

To suggest that if voluntary euthanasia legislation were enacted it would be necessary for someone signing the declaration to be declared as of sound mind is unrealistic. A similar argument could be raised about making a Will or any other important decision, for example, consent to or refusal of an operation. Psychiatrists (if they can avoid it), do not declare a person as being of sound mind; the assumption is that he is of sound mind unless there are compelling reasons for concluding that he is not.

There is no great difficulty in recognizing the mentally ill patient who is in a state of mental depression, and no one is suggesting that a patient in that condition who merely expressed a wish to die should be given euthanasia. Help of this kind could only be given in the circumstances defined in the Voluntary Euthanasia Bill presented to the House of Lords in April, 1969. The patient must be suffering from 'a serious physical illness or impairment reasonably thought in the patient's case to be incurable and expected to cause him severe distress or render him incapable of rational existence'.

The Elderly It is reasonable to assume that most people accept with serenity the prospect of death: also that some of the elderly hope that their dying will not be unduly prolonged by modern medical developments *without* their having any choice in the matter. Although opponents of voluntary euthanasia often contend that 'nobody wants to die', the BMA Report admits that 'there is no doubt that some may desire it, especially if denied the support of relatives and friends'. This should cause no surprise. When all the dignity, beauty and meaning of life has vanished and the only prospect is prolonged distress, these elderly people have acquired the wisdom to regard death as a friend rather than an enemy. What is so wrong about helping them towards death when that is their expressed wish?

To suggest, as the Report does, that 'what is needed here is not a change in the law but a change in the attitude of people towards their dying elderly relatives and friends' is quite unrealistic. Relatives and friends who have had little or no time or affection for their old people are not likely to become good samaritans when death is approaching. And what about the many, many old people who have no relatives and are so terribly alone?

The motives and devotion of those who keep old people alive 'by kindness, good nutrition and good nursing' deserve the utmost respect and admiration, but could it not be recognized that, in some cases, the greatest kindness would be to comply with the wish of the old person who says 'I have suffered enough'?

The Report contends that the argument that the elderly are 'kept alive by the use of drugs' has been grossly exaggerated; and that there is much evidence to show that even the most potent remedies may become 'relatively ineffective' in old age. This is an extraordinary argument. Apparently doctors are to be excused from the accusation because the drugs they use are ineffective.

Whether the accusation is 'grossly exaggerated' is open to question. Few of those who saw the television programme 'Death Unto Himself Alone' (BBC-1, 14 November 1967) are likely to forget it. It featured a hostel for the dying with very old people who, according to the nurse, were 'waiting their time'. What was so shocking was to hear the nurse explain that should any of those unfortunates have a recurrence of some illness for which they had received treatment in another hospital, they would be sent back there for treatment and then returned to the hostel once more to 'wait their time' – for a few more weeks, months or, possibly, years.

There is, unfortunately, justification for believing that this determination to prolong life to the last gasp is not uncommon. But surely it should be conceded that when all hope of cure has been abandoned, a patient should have the right to say 'Enough'?

The Report points out that elderly people are liable to varying degrees of mental impairment and that their alertness may fluctuate from day to day, particularly if diminished by toxic complications of illness. 'At such times, they could not be expected to understand the issues involved in euthanasia.'

But on what grounds should it be assumed that an old person who, in a state of clear consciousness, has shown a steadfast wish to die, should have abrogated that wish when he becomes confused?

The proposals for legalization of voluntary euthanasia provide that a declaration must have been signed and witnessed 30 days or more previously when the signatory appreciated its significance. And, of course, euthanasia could only be administered when the alternative, in the opinion of a doctor and consultant, was severe distress or the incapability of rational existence·

Advance Declaration   The Report seeks to dismiss lightly the arguments in favour of an advance declaration of the wish for voluntary euthanasia in certain specified circumstances, i.e. if there should be no reasonable prospect of recovery from physical or mental illness *likely to cause severe distress* or to render the patient incapable of rational existence. The Panel, having omitted the important phrase in italics, then warn of the danger of life being terminated 'when a degree of dementia was present'. There is no mistaking the state of a seriously demented patient. Such patients are kept going for two years and more in psychogeriatric wards by kindness, good nutrition and good nursing. In such cases the dividing line, once unclear, has long since been passed. To refer to euthanasia as 'a decision to kill' is to imply that putting an end to the vegetative mechanism which goes on ticking long after the last signs of the life of the mind have passed is on a par with killing the mentally alive subject. If, for the emotive words used we were to substitute 'euthanasia, the provision of a merciful release . . .' it would be seen that this would be far from being 'an intolerable burden upon the doctor'.

The Report refers in several places to the responsibility resting on doctors, and claims that euthanasia would be an intolerable addition to such responsibilities. This carries no conviction. Doctors are constantly taking life-and-death decisions, e.g. whether to operate on a severely ill patient who might die under the operation, whether to carry out a radical excision or something less, and so forth. They are trained and educated to carry such responsibilities and do so courageously. Mankind cannot escape life-and-death responsibilities, e.g. in wars, and doctors are very far from being the tender plants which the Report so sentimentally supposes.

The Report acknowledges that 'It is natural to desire to die with dignity' but adds an extremely insensitive statement that 'in advanced age bodily functions and control, for example, of bladder and bowels, may become impaired' when 'failing mental powers may lessen the patient's awareness of his plight'. This is partly true but who can face such a future with equanimity? To say that 'It would be primarily the distress of the relatives that would be relieved by euthanasia in such instances' is no argument for not helping the patient. The relief of the relatives' distress would be incidental to the main consideration – the welfare of the patient and respect for his previously declared wishes. But it is not only when we have drifted into mindlessness that we are liable to degrading accidents of impaired bodily control. Incontinence afflicts those very well aware of their condition, and causes much mental distress.

Possible New Cures   It is true that 'advances in medicine are taking place all the time and diseases which have no remedy one year may have effective treatment the next'. But what comfort does that bring to the dying patient who wishes for release now from his suffering? It is no argument to say that people should not be helped now because it *may* be possible to help them next year – or the decade after next.

Inadequate Facilities   No one is likely to disagree that 'our community has devoted too little of its resources to the care of the elderly and chronic sick'. It must be realized, however, resources for this purpose have to be obtained in competition with a vast range of other claims within the Health Service, and the Health Service itself has to compete with other claims by the community for funds. Furthermore, there are some patients who would not wish their chronicity to be dragged out even longer and more distressingly. They want, simply, an end.

Medical Education   This Society welcomes the BMA statement that there has been too little teaching in medical schools of 'perimortal morbidity': also that 'the problems of death and euthanasia should command the attention of teachers and students alike'. But even if more teaching were to begin immediately, it would be many years before half the practising doctors and their patients could benefit from it.

The contention that 'a change in the law would hamper changes in attitudes' is surprising. Legislation which gave the option of voluntary euthanasia to doctors and patients would surely stimulate further study and discussion from which new attitudes would be likely to evolve. Indeed, in the National Opinion Polls, previously referred to, 35·8 % of the G.P.'s who replied said that they would be prepared to administer euthanasia if legally permissible. Medical attitudes are not so rigid as implied. There have been notable changes over the years, for example, towards birth control and even the use of anaesthetics.

Errors in Medical Diagnosis and Prognosis The Panel contend that it would be impossible to provide adequate safeguards in any euthanasia legislation. 'Medical diagnosis . . . will always contain an element of fallibility . . .' 'Mistakes would inevitably be made.' All decisions are fallible and it is remarkable that doctors should put forward this argument, as their daily work is constantly based on probabilities. The argument seems to be based on the rooted assumption that death is the Great Enemy. Are there not circumstances in which a decision to carry out euthanasia would clearly be for the benefit of the patient? The answer is, of course, yes. The benefits of such a course of action would have to be weighed against the possibilities of error: the decision would depend on a clinical judgment of a kind which doctors are constantly making. It is right to say that many of the errors of judgment made in curative medicine can be corrected, and it would have been equally correct to say that many of them, e.g., the decision to amputate, are irreversible.

However, the argument about fallibility is one-sided and unfair. Clinical decisions are often what one might call a toss-up – they depend on estimates of probability in which the balance is often rather even. The decision to carry out euthanasia, in the circumstances in which the Society advocates its admissibility, would be one in which the probabilities of benefit would enormously outweigh the probability of an error.

The Report says 'It must always be a clinical decision when to regard death as imminent.' Of course: this is a decision that doctors are specifically trained to make and experienced in making.

Many doctors do not share the Panel's view on the impossibility of adequate safeguards. In the combined National Opinion Polls (previously referred to) opinion was fairly evenly divided. In reply to the question 'If voluntary euthanasia were to be sanctioned by law in certain circumstances, do you think that appropriate safeguards (as simple as possible) could be devised?', 44·3% of those who replied answered 'Yes' and 43·5% 'No'.

If the safeguards already proposed (including agreement between doctor and consultant) are not considered adequate, it should not be beyond the powers of the medical and legal professions to produce others which would be acceptable to the community.

Validity of a Request for Euthanasia There is no disagreement with the Panel that 'a request for euthanasia would have to be made freely by a person who understood the nature of his request'. This is exactly what has been proposed. But they then go on to suggest that, for one reason or another, a person would never be able to make a decision which would not be suspect. The basic idea seems to be that if a patient decides he wants to go on living, this is a sound and rational decision although such a decision might well be irrational and based, for instance, on a morbid and pathological fear of death. Whatever the reason, the patient's wishes should be the paramount consideration and, if he wants to go on living, then no question of euthanasia could possibly arise.

But if a patient wants to die, why should his decision be suspect? Why cannot the Panel accept that it may be made on its merits? Earlier in their Report they concede that 'there is no doubt that some may desire it' (death). Most people, we believe, would regard this as a logical attitude when the alternative is prolonged dying and distress.

Confidence in Doctors and Nurses   The Panel produced no arguments whatever in support of its contention that the patient's confidence in his doctor and nurse 'would be placed in jeopardy if their roles were extended to include the task of ending life'.

If voluntary euthanasia were legalized, everyone would know – doctors, nurses and patients – that nothing could be done contrary to the expressed wishes of the patient. As things stand now, there is a genuine fear, admitted by the Panel, on the part of many old people that life will be prolonged by modern medical developments without their having any choice in the matter.

It was made perfectly clear in a recent series of three television programmes on the subject that patient-doctor relationship leaves much to be desired. If patients knew that, should they be dying of an incurable disease and their suffering became intolerable they could rely upon their doctor to give them final release, they could face the future with greater confidence and hope. As the law now stands they must have grave doubts, which will not be lessened by the BMA Report.

The Panel appear to underestimate the intelligence and common-sense of the public. They are far less likely to fear the doctor as an 'executioner' than to welcome him as a compassionate friend-in-need who will mercifully end the life of one who, in the terms of the proposed legislation, has been certified by two physicians as suffering from a serious illness or impairment thought to be incurable and likely to cause him severe distress or render him incapable of rational existence.

The kind and compassionate doctor even now goes a long way: patients would have more respect and trust if they could be brought to believe that their doctor was more responsive to their wishes. The Panel writes as if doctors are always trusted and never feared as things are now: this is not so. It is notorious that patients so fear what doctors will do to them that they are commonly very late in reporting the first symptoms of a growing cancer. It seems absurd to suppose that patients would fear doctors more if they (the patients) had more control over them, and were not so totally in their hands as now.

No one would disagree with the Panel's definition of the tradition of medicine – to cure, heal and to relieve suffering. But it is the relief of suffering of those who can neither be healed nor cured that is the sole purpose of the advocates of voluntary euthanasia. To say that 'a law to permit euthanasia might damage the vocational aspect of the work and indirectly affect recruitment to the profession' shows professional egocentricity at its worst. Presumably patients are to drag out their suffering in order to maintain medical recruitment!

Other Possible Effects of Euthanasia Legislation   The suggestion that relatives would have to bear the responsibility for the life-or-death decision is utterly unjustifiable. Anyone who has read the Bills presented to Parliament knows perfectly well that the decision is the *sole* prerogative of the patient.

It seems that the Panel want to attribute different motives to relatives – pressure to end a patient's life; pressure to prevent his requesting merciful release. The Report supplies its own answer to the question – 'the welfare of the patient must be the over-riding consideration'.

There is no justification for the suggestion that the legalization of voluntary euthanasia for adults might eventually be extended to include children. Grossly deformed and mentally deficient children present a terrible problem to the medical profession and to parents. But the problem exists now; it is not created by the demand for voluntary euthanasia for adults facing prolonged dying and distress, nor would it be affected by relevant legislation. Doctors are already compelled to face this awful problem and one doctor has said on television that when 'monsters' are born no steps are taken to 'give them life'.

If there are to be any proposals to cope with this problem, they will have to be dealt with on their merits and approved or rejected by the community through their elected representatives to Parliament.

Final Considerations   The Panel seeks to deny a person's 'right to die' because, they allege, it conflicts with a fundamentally different principle, 'the right to live'.

There is, in fact, no conflict here. The right to die is logically a part of the right to live. If there is no right to end one's life, then it is not a 'right' to live but merely an inescapable obligation. As it is not a criminal offence to commit or attempt to commit suicide, the law concedes the right of the individual to end his own life.

But the argument is really irrelevant. Voluntary euthanasia would do nothing whatever to take away the right to live. At the risk, however, of being accused of evading the issue, an answer must be given to the question 'If the law were changed, would the unsuccessful suicide be in a position to prosecute doctors and nurses who had interfered with this newly proposed basic right – the right to die?'

Firstly, the legalization of voluntary euthanasia would have no bearing on the position. The danger of prosecution would be no greater or less than now. Secondly, as to the present legal position, we are advised that if a person left a note saying that he was committing suicide and forbidding any inferference, he could prosecute anyone who did interfere.

The Panel acknowledge that a minority of those who are resuscitated after a suicide attempt regret the resuscitation and make a second attempt. It could be argued that a deliberate attempt to end one's life, accompanied by a solemn declaration that this was a well-considered act, should be accepted by doctors, and that the individual should have complete sovereignty over his own life.

In the concluding paragraphs of the Report, reasoned argument has been abandoned in favour of emotion and misrepresentation. Having defined euthanasia in their opening paragraph as 'a good death' or 'a gentle death' and 'the deliberate termination of the life of a person suffering from a distressing irremediable disease', they now prefer 'a licence for the killing of human beings'.

To them, 'It seems an anachronism to introduce it at a time when capital punishment has been abolished and the young are openly moving towards pacifism'. What on earth has capital punishment got to do with humanitarian legislation? And if the young are moving towards pacifism, is it not most likely that the reason is because they are becoming *more* humanitarian and more concerned with the suffering which war brings?

For good measure the Panel bring in the Nazis who, it is alleged, practised euthanasia 'to improve the race'. Were the Nazis ever concerned with the gentle death of a person suffering from a distressing irremediable disease, which is what the discussion of voluntary euthanasia is all about?

We agree that 'civilizations are sometimes judged by their care of the poor, the weak, the elderly and the infirm'. As the Panel well know, our booklet *A Plea for Voluntary Euthanasia* states:

> The Society believes that care of the old, the sick and the dying should be a paramount obligation upon any humane society. No expense or care should be spared in providing for their physical well-being and peace of mind.

But this Society also believes that when they face painful, distressing and prolonged dying, they should have the right to gentle, dignified death.

There are many doctors who disagree with the Panel's view that 'euthanasia cannot be accepted by the medical profession' and amongst the educated public the question is an open one, as shown by the House of Lords debate on Lord Raglan's Bill.

Discussion of this vital subject will continue and increase. It is a great pity that the Panel approached their task with their minds already made up and that, to quote *Nature* (29 January 1971), 'they were so timorous and unimaginative in suggesting how a real problem might be made to go away'.

The Voluntary Euthanasia Society
13 Prince of Wales Terrace
London W8

APPENDIX C

Voluntary Euthanasia Bill (1969)

Explanatory Memorandum

General

The main purpose of the Bill is to authorize physicians to give euthanasia
to a patient who is thought on reasonable grounds to be suffering from an
irremediable physical condition of a distressing character, and who has,
not less than 30 days previously, made a declaration requesting the
administration of euthanasia in certain specified circumstances one or
more of which has eventuated.

Clause 1 provides that a physician may administer euthanasia to a
'qualified patient' who has made a declaration in the form set out in the
schedule. A qualified patient is defined as a patient over the age of majority
who has been certified by two physicians, one being of consultant status, to
be apparently suffering from an irremediable condition. Subsection (2)
defines the expressions used in the Bill.

Clause 2 provides that a declaration shall come into force 30 days after
being made, and shall remain in force for 3 years. A declaration re-executed
within the 12 months preceding its expiry date shall remain in force for life,
unless revoked.

Clause 3 provides that a declaration may be revoked at any time.

Clause 4 provides that before euthanasia may be given to a mentally responsible patient the physician in charge must ascertain to the best of his
ability that the declaration and steps proposed to be taken under it accord
with the patient's wishes. Subsection (2) provides that a nurse, acting on the
directions of a physician, may cause euthanasia to be administered to a
patient, and subsection (3) provides that no physician or nurse who is
opposed on principle to euthanasia shall be required to take any steps in its
administration.

Clause 5 protects physicians and nurses who act in good faith in the
belief that their actions are in accordance with a patient's declaration or
further requests made under the Act and provides that they shall not be in
breach of any professional oath by administering euthanasia.

Clause 6 provides that a person who conceals, destroys, falsifies or forges a declaration commits an offence punishable by life imprisonment, and that an attesting witness who wilfully makes a false statement commits an offence punishable by up to 7 years' imprisonment.

Clause 7 provides that euthanasia shall not, except in limited circumstances, invalidate any insurance policy.

Clause 8 declares that all terminal patients are entitled to receive whatever quantity of drugs may be required to keep them entirely free from pain; and that in a case where severe distress cannot be alleviated by painkilling drugs, the patient is entitled, if he so desires, to be made and kept entirely unconscious. The section applies to patients whether or not they have made any declaration, and is expressed to be for the removal of doubt as to the existing state of the law.

Clause 9 provides for the Secretary of State for Social Services to make regulations specifying classes of persons entitled or not entitled to witness a declaration, defining the duties of hospital physicians having responsibility for patients in relation to euthanasia, regulating the custody of declarations, and for any other purpose.

Clause 10 contains the short title and extent of the Act.

Arrangement of Clauses

Clause

1. Authorization of euthanasia.
2. Declaration made in advance
3. Mode of revocation
4. Duties and right of physicians and nurses
5. Protection for physicians and nurses
6. Offences
7. Insurance policies
8. Administration of drugs to patients suffering severe distress
9. Power to make regulations
10. Short title and extent

   Schedule Form of declaration

Voluntary Euthanasia

A BILL INTITULED

AD 1969 An Act to provide in certain circumstances for the administration of euthanasia to persons who request it and who are suffering from an irremediable condition, and to enable persons to request in advance the administration of euthanasia in the event of their suffering from such a condition at a future date.

Be it enacted by the Queen's most Excellent Majesty,

by and with the consent of the Lords Spiritual and Temporal, and Commons, in this present Parliament assembled, and by the authority of the same, as follows:

Authorization of euthanasia

1 (1) Subject to the provisions of this Act, it shall be lawful for a physician to administer euthanasia to a qualified patient who has made a declaration that is for the time being in force.

(2) For the purposes of this Act:

'physician' means a registered medical practitioner;

'euthanasia' means the painless inducement of death;

'qualified patient' means a patient over the age of majority in respect of whom two physicians (one being of consultant status) have certified in writing that the patient appears to them to be suffering from an irremediable condition;

'irremediable condition' means a serious physical illness or impairment reasonably thought in the patient's case to be incurable and expected to cause him severe distress or render him incapable of rational existence:

'declaration' means a witnessed declaration in writing made substantially in the form set out in the schedule to this Act.

Declaration made in advance

2 (1) Subject to the provisions of this section, a declaration shall come into force 30 days after being made and shall remain in force (unless revoked) for 3 years.

(2) A declaration re-executed within the 12 months preceding its expiry date shall remain in force (unless revoked) during the lifetime of the declarant.

Mode of revocation

3. A declaration may be revoked at any time by destruction or by notice of cancellation shown on its face, effected (in either case) by the declarant or to his order.

Duties and rights of physicians and nurses

4 (1) Before causing euthanasia to be administered to a mentally responsible patient the physician in charge shall ascertain to his reasonable satisfaction that the declaration and all steps proposed to be taken under it accord with the patient's wishes.

(2) Euthanasia shall be deemed to be administered by a physician if treatment prescribed by a physician is given to the patient by a state registered or state enrolled nurse.

(3) No person shall be under any duty, whether by contract or by any statutory or other legal requirement, to participate in any treatment authorized by this Act to which he has a conscientious objection.

Protection for
physicians and
nurses

5 (1) A physician or nurse who, acting in good faith, causes euthanasia to be administered to a qualified patient in accordance with what the person so acting believes to be the patient's declaration and wishes shall not be guilty of any offence.

(2) Physicians and nurses who have taken part in the administration of euthanasia shall be deemed not to be in breach of any professional oath or affirmation.

Offences

6 (1) It shall be an offence punishable on indictment by a sentence of life imprisonment wilfully to conceal, destroy, falsify or forge a declaration with intent to create a false impression of another person's wishes with regard to euthanasia.

(2) A person signing a declaration by way of attestation who wilfully puts his signature to a statement he knows to be false shall be deemed to have committed an offence under section 2 of the Perjury Act 1911.

1911 c. 6

Insurance
policies

7. No policy of insurance that has been in force for 12 months shall be vitiated by the administration of euthanasia to the insured.

Administration
of drugs to
patients
suffering
severe distress

8. For the removal of doubt it is declared that a patient suffering from an irremediable condition reasonably thought in his case to be terminal shall be entitled to the administration of whatever quantity of drugs may be required to keep him free from pain, and such a patient in whose case severe distress cannot be otherwise relieved shall, if he so requests, be entitled to drugs rendering him continuously unconscious.

Power to make
regulations

9 (1) The Secretary of State for Social Services shall make regulations under this Act by statutory instrument for determining classes of persons who may or may not sign a declaration by way of attestation, for regulating the custody of declarations, for appointing (with their consent) hospital physicians having responsibility in relation to patients who have made or wish to make a declaration, and for the prescribing of any matters he may think fit to prescribe for the purposes of this Act.

(2) Any statutory instrument made under this Act shall be subject to annulment in pursuance of a resolution of either House of Parliament.

Short title and
extent

10 (1) This Act may be cited as the Voluntary Euthanasia Act 1969.

(2) This Act does not extend to Northern Ireland.

Schedule

FORM OF DECLARATION UNDER THE VOLUNTARY EUTHANASIA ACT 1969

Declaration made   19   [and re-executed
                                    19   ]
    by
    of

I DECLARE that I subscribe to the code set out under the following articles:

A. If I should at any time suffer from a serious physical illness or impairment reasonably thought in my case to be incurable and expected to cause me severe distress or render me incapable of rational existence, I request the administration of euthanasia at a time or in circumstances to be indicated or specified by me or, if it is apparent that I have become incapable of giving directions, at the discretion of the physician in charge of my case.

B. In the event of my suffering from any of the conditions specified above, I request that no active steps should be taken, and in particular that no resuscitatory techniques should be used, to prolong my life or restore me to consciousness.

C. This declaration is to remain in force unless I revoke it, which I may do at any time, and any request I may make concerning action to be taken or withheld in connection with this declaration will be made without further formalities.

I WISH it to be understood that I have confidence in the good faith of my relatives and physicians, and fear degeneration and indignity far more than I fear premature death. I ask and authorize the physician in charge of my case to bear these statements in mind when considering what my wishes would be in any uncertain situation.

SIGNED

[SIGNED ON RE-EXECUTION]

WE TESTIFY that the above-named declarant *[signed] *[was unable to write but assented to] this declaration in our presence, and appeared to appreciate its significance. We do not know of any pressure being brought on him to make a declaration, and we believe it is made by his own wish. So far as we are aware, we are entitled to attest this declaration and do not stand to benefit by the death of the declarant.

Signed by	Signed by
of	of
[Signed by	[Signed by
of	of
on re-execution]	on re-execution]

---

* Strike out whichever words do not apply.

Suggested Non-statutory Declaration

TO MY FAMILY AND MY PHYSICIAN:

This Statement is made by me ....
at a time when I am of sound mind and after careful consideration.

If the time comes when I can no longer take part in decisions for my own future, let this Statement stand as the testament to my wishes:

If there is no reasonable prospect of my recovery from physical or mental illness or impairment expected to cause me severe distress or to render me incapable of rational existence, I request that I be allowed to die and not be kept alive by artificial means and that I receive whatever quantity of drugs may be required to keep me free from pain or distress even if the moment of death is hastened.

Signed......................

Dated......................

Witnessed by:

1. .... 2. ....

of .... of ....

....

NOTE: Witnesses should not be members of the family

NOTES

I *History of Suicide and Euthanasia*

1. P. Sainsbury, *Suicide in London*, Chapman and Hall 1955.
2. E. Stengel, *Suicide and Attempted Suicide*, Penguin 1964, p. 55.
3. Glanville Williams, *The Sanctity of Life and the Criminal Law* (cited hereafter as *Sanctity of Life*), Faber and Faber 1958, p.225.
4. P. Bohannan, *African Homicide and Suicide*, Princeton University Press 1960.
5. Elizabeth Huxley, *The Flame Trees of Thika*, Chatto and Windus 1959, p.112.
6. *Ought Suicide to be a Crime?*, Church Information Office 1959, Appendix D.
7. Stengel, op. cit., pp.57f.
8. Judg. 16.23–30.
9. I Sam. 31.3–6.
10. II Sam. 1.6–10.
11. Judg. 9.53f.; II Sam. 17.23; I Kings 16.18.
12. II Macc. 14.41–46.
13. E.g. II Macc. 6.11; 7.1–42.
14. Tobit 3.7–17.
15. Ex. 20.13; Deut. 5.17; Gen. 9.5f.
16. Job 2.9f.
17. Josephus, *Jewish War* III, 362–82.
18. Ibid. VII, 275–406.
19. Matt. 27.5; cf. Acts 1.16–25.
20. Acts 16.27.
21. I. Jakobovits, *Jewish Medical Ethics*, Philosophical Library, New York, 1959, p.123.
22. Hastings' *Encyclopaedia of Religion and Ethics*, 1921 ed., vol. 12, p.38.
23. R. Gillon, 'Suicide and Voluntary Euthanasia: Historical Perspective', in A. B. Downing, ed., *Euthanasia and the Right to Death* (cited hereafter as Downing, *Euthanasia*), Peter Owen 1969, pp.173–92; Williams, *Sanctity of Life*, pp.224–9.
24. Quoted by Gillon, art. cit., p.174.
25. Epictetus, *Dissertations* I, xi.16.
26. Suetonius, *Lives of the Caesars* II, 99.
27. Pliny, *Epistles* I, 22.
28. H. E. Sigerist, *A History of Medicine*, Oxford University Press, Vol. 2, 1961, p.302.
29. D. Gourevitch, *Bulletin of the History of Medicine* 43, 1969, pp. 501–18.

30. Sigerist, op. cit., vol. 2, p.303.

31. Ibid., p.312 n.8.

32. F. Rosner and S. Munter, *Annals of Internal Medicine* 63, 1965, p.317.

33. Sigerist, op. cit., vol. 2, p.303.

34. Ibid., p.305.

35. P. Brown, *Augustine of Hippo*, Faber and Faber 1967, p.229.

36. Augustine, *City of God* XV.iv.

37. Williams, *Sanctity of Life*, p.232.

38. Ibid., p.245.

39. Thomas Aquinas, *Summa Theologica*, Part II.2, Second Number, Question 59, Article 3; Question 64, Article 5.

40. E. Stengel and N. G. Cook, *Attempted Suicide*, Oxford University Press 1958.

41. P. S. Sainsbury, *Suicide in London*, Chapman and Hall 1955.

42. Stengel, op. cit., pp.55–63.

43. Williams, *Sanctity of Life*, pp.224–76.

44. Sigerist, op. cit., vol. 2, p.299.

45. R. M. Clay, *The Mediaeval Hospitals of England*, reprinted Cass 1966, pp.149f., 218.

46. W. S. C. Copeman, *Doctors and Diseases in Tudor Times*, Dawsons 1960, pp. 121f.

47. Thomas More, *Utopia*, 1516, Part II, ch. 7 (trans. with modernized spelling; cf. C. Killick Millard, *Euthanasia*, C. W. Daniel 1931, p.14).

48. Francis Bacon, *Of the Advancement of Learning*, 1605, Book II, x. 7.

49. Williams, *Sanctity of Life*, p.277; Gillon, art. cit. in Downing, *Euthanasia*, p.177.

50. F. Henschen, *The History of Diseases*, Eng. trans., Longmans 1966, p.288.

51. L. A. Tollemache, *Fortnightly Review*, 1873, no. 19, p.218.

52. *The Spectator*, 1873, no. 46, p.206.

53. Ibid., p.240.

54. Gillon, art. cit., p.183.

55. F. A. W. Gisborne, *Democracy on Trial*, Longmans Green 1928.

56. W. R. Inge, *Christian Ethics and Modern Problems*, Hodder and Stoughton 1930, p.373.

57. Peter Green, *The Problem of Right Conduct*, Longmans Green 1931, p.283.

58. C. K. Millard, *Euthanasia*, C. W. Daniel 1931.

59. *Hansard (Lords)*, 1936/7, vol. 103, cols. 466–506.

60. *Hansard (Lords)*, 1950, vol. 169, cols. 551–9.

61. Williams, *Sanctity of Life*, p.311.

62. *Human Rights*, United Kingdom Committee for Human Rights Year, Heinemann 1967, p.199 n. 2.

63. Ibid., p.202.

64. Mary R. Barrington, 'Apologia for Suicide' in Downing, *Euthanasia*, pp.152–72; here p.167.

65. Yale Kasimar, 'Euthanasia Legislation: some Non-religious Objections', ibid., pp.85–133; Glanville Williams, 'Euthanasia Legislation: A Rejoinder to the Non-religious Objections', ibid., pp.134–47.
66. *British Medical Journal* (hereafter cited as *BMJ*), 1969.4, p.229.
67. Ibid., p.554.
68. *Nature* 229, 1971, p.289.
69. *New Society*, 28 Jan. 1971, p.133.
70. *New Statesman*, 22 Jan. 1971, p.109.
71. Kasimar, art. cit., p.128 n. 88.
72. Ibid., p.129 nn. 89–92.
73. Ibid., p.129 n. 93.
74. Williams, *Sanctity of Life*, p.293.
75. Kasimar, art. cit., p.129 n. 94.
76. Ibid., p.129 n. 95.
77. *Royal Commission on Capital Punishment*, Report (1953), Cmd. No. 8932, p.iii.
78. Ibid., para. 179.
79. Williams, *Sanctity of Life*, p.293.

II *The Case for Legislation*

1. *A Plea for Legislation to Permit Voluntary Euthanasia*, Voluntary Euthanasia Society 1970.
2. Downing, *Euthanasia*, and Glanville Williams, *Sanctity of Life*, pp.277–312.
3. J. M. Hinton, *Dying*, Pelican 1967, p.53.
4. A. N. Exton-Smith, *The Lancet*, 1961.2, p.305.
5. J. M. Hinton in *Medicine in Old Age*, ed. J. N. Agate, Pitman 1965.
6. Cicely Saunders, *Proceedings of the Royal Society of Medicine* 56, 1963, pp. 195–7, and 'The Nature and Management of Terminal Pain' in *Matters of Life and Death*, ed. E. Shotter, Darton, Longman and Todd 1970, pp.15–26.
7. J. M. Hinton, *Quarterly Journal of Medicine* 32, 1963, p.1.
8. *Report on a National Survey concerning Patients with Cancer Nursed at Home*. Joint National Cancer Survey Committee. Marie Curie Memorial 1952.
9. J. Aitken-Swan, *The Practitioner* 183, 1959, p.64.
10. E. Wilkes, *The Lancet*, 1965.1, p.799.
11. W. St C. Symmers, *BMJ* 1968.1, p.442.
12. Ibid., p.576.
13. Hinton, *Dying*, pp.71f.
14. Joseph Fletcher, *Situation Ethics: The New Morality*, SCM Press 1966; *Morals and Medicine*, Gollancz 1955; *Moral Responsibility: Situation Ethics at Work*, SCM Press 1967.
15. Joseph Fletcher in *Who Shall Live?*, ed. K. Vaux, Fortress Press, Philadelphia 1970.
16. *Parliamentary Debates (House of Lords)*, 1936, vol. 103, cols. 562–3.

17. *Decisions about Life and Death*, Church Assembly Board for Social Responsibility 1965.
18. L. Weatherhead, *The Christian Agnostic*, Hodder and Stoughton 1965, p.187.
19. W. R. Inge, *Christian Ethics and Moral Problems*, p.373.
20. P. Green, *The Problem of Right Conduct*, p.283.

III   Legal and Ethical Aspects

1. G. P. Fletcher, *Journal of the American Medical Association* 203, 1968, p.65.
2. Williams, *Sanctity of Life*, p.283.
3. Ibid., p.290.
4. Quoted by Williams, ibid., p.289.
5. Ibid., p.292.
6. *BMJ* 1957.1, pp.712, 771, 889, 954; 1957.2, p.303.
7. Williams, op. cit., p.290.
8. See pp. 94f., 122f., 124ff., 134ff., 141ff.
9. Fletcher, art. cit., p.65.
10. Williams, op. cit., p.291.
11. See Appendix A, p.153.
12. Y. Kasimar in Downing, *Euthanasia*, pp.119–21 n. 19.
13. D. W. Meyers, *The Human Body and the Law*, Edinburgh University Press 1970, p.145.
14. Ibid., pp.147f.
15. A legal definition quoted by Meyers, op. cit., p.72.
16. *The Problem of Euthanasia*, see Appendix A, p.156.
17. J. Fletcher, *Morals and Medicine*, p.172.
18. H. E. Sigerist, *A History of Medicine*, vol. 2, p.301.
19. H. Roberts, *Euthanasia and Other Aspects of Life and Death*, Constable 1936, pp.15–17.
20. I. Stewart, *The Lancet*, 1960.2, p.919.
21. L. Banks, *Bulletin of the New York Academy of Medicine* 26, 1950, pp.297–301.
22. Millard, *Euthanasia*, pp.32–5.
23. Williams, *Sanctity of Life*, p.303.
24. Ibid., pp.308, 303 n.
25. Williams in Downing, *Euthanasia*, p.146.
26. Williams, *Sanctity of Life*, p.297.
27. Williams in Downing, *Euthanasia*, p.143.
28. Williams, *Sanctity of Life*, p.277.
29. Ibid., pp.302–9.
30. Ibid., p.302.
31. Ibid., p.277.
32. Ibid., p.304.
33. Ibid., p.303.
34. Ibid., p.309.

35. Ibid., p.311.
36. Ibid., p.309.
37. Ibid., p.310.
38. *Memorandum of Voluntary Euthanasia Society*, 1970, p.10.
39. J. Fletcher in Downing, *Euthanasia*, p.67.
40. Ibid., pp.65f.

IV   *Medical Aspects*

1. R. Gillon, 'Suicide and Voluntary Euthanasia: Historical Perspective', in Downing, *Euthanasia*, pp.173–92.
2. G. A. Gresham, 'A Time to be Born and a Time to Die', ibid., pp. 148–51.
3. E. Slater, 'Death: the Biological Aspect', ibid., pp.56f.
4. S. L. H. Smith, *Medical News-Tribune*, 11 December 1970.
5. S. L. H. Smith, ibid., 13 November 1970.
6. A. R. P. Walker, *South African Medical Journal* 42, 1968, p.944.
7. Slater in Downing, *Euthanasia*, p.56.
8. Walker, loc. cit.
9. J. Hinton, *Dying*, p.54.
10. D. Harman, *Medical News-Tribune*, 11 October 1968.
11. *The Times*, 8 November 1966.
12. Ps.90.10 (New English Bible).
13. *The Guardian*, 25 April 1967.
14. *BMJ* 1971.1, p.289.
15. A. Paton, *BMJ* 1969.3, p.591.
16. Lord Platt, *BMJ* 1969.4, p.229.
17. See p.29 above, quoting *BMJ* 1968.1, pp.442 and 576.
18. *A Plea for Legislation to Permit Voluntary Euthanasia*, p.5.
19. L. Lusanga in *The Dying Patient*, ed. O. G. Brim and others, Russell Sage Foundation, New York 1970, pp.87f.
20. K. Vickery, *Medical News*, 12 September 1969, p.6.
21. G. Thomson, *The Lancet*, 1969.2, p.1353.
22. John Agate, *The Practice of Geriatrics*, Heinemann, 2nd ed., 1970, pp.489–510; quotation from p.497.
23. *The Guardian*, 25 April 1967, quoted by Downing, *Euthanasia*, p.16.
24. T. C. Everson, *Annals of the New York Academy of Science* 114, 1964, p.721.
25. D. Nelson, *BMJ* 1960.2, p.670.
26. M. F. A. Woodruff, *The Lancet*, 1964.2, p.265.
27. G. Klein and others, *BMJ* 1970.4, pp.418ff.
28. C. E. Koop and others, *Surgery* 56, 1964, p.726.
29. H. J. G. Bloom and others, *BMJ* 1962.2, p.213.
30. I. P. Beswick and others, *BMJ* 1963.2, p.930.
31. M. Sutton, *BMJ* 1960.2, p.1132.
32. M. Chauffard, *Bulletin de l'Académie de médecine* (Paris) 107, 1932, p.97.
33. A. N. Exton-Smith, *The Lancet*, 1961.2, p.305.

34. Cicely Saunders, *Care of the Dying*, Macmillan 1959; *The Lancet*, 1961.2, p.548.

35. Id., *Proceedings of the Royal Society of Medicine* 56, 1963, p.195.

36. M. Schott, *BMJ* 1967.3, p.433.

37. G. A. Gresham in Downing, *Euthanasia*, p.148.

38. D. McAlpine and others, *Multiple Sclerosis*, Oxford University Press 1965, pp.186, 191.

39. H. C. Bethune and others, *The Lancet*, 1961.2, p.1419.

40. W. Lewin, *Proceedings of the Royal Society of Medicine* 60, 1967, p.1208.

41. J. J. Walsh, ibid., p.1212.

42. D. Hill, ibid., p.1232.

43. Lord Cohen, ibid., p.1200, 1195.

44. M. A. Heasman and L. Lipworth, *Accuracy of Certification of Cause of Death*, Studies on Medical and Population Subjects 20, 1966, Registrar General's Office, London (reviewed in *BMJ* 1966.2, p.1465).

45. T. W. Meade and others, *Proceedings of the Royal Society of Medicine* 61, 1968, p.451.

46. M. D. Rawson, *The Lancet*, 1965.1, p.698.

47. E. Slater in Downing, *Euthanasia*, p.49.

48. Agate, *The Practice of Geriatrics*, p.56.

49. L. A. Wilson and others, *The Lancet*, 1962.2, p.841.

50. See n. 44 above.

51. Downing, *Euthanasia*, p.33; Joseph Fletcher, ibid., p.67; G. P. Fletcher, ibid., p.71; Glanville Williams, ibid., p.134.

52. A. N. Exton-Smith, *The Lancet*, 1961.2, p.305.

53. Agate, op. cit., p.506.

54. F. Camps, *Matters of Life and Death*, p.5.

55 O. G. Brim and others, *The Dying Patient*, p.131.

56. A. E. Clark-Kennedy, *Man, Medicine and Morality*, Faber and Faber 1969, p.204.

57. R. H. Micks, *Materia Medica*, J. and A. Churchill, 9th ed., 1965, p.32.

58. A. Grollman, *Pharmacology and Therapeutics*, Kimpton, 5th ed., 1962, p.132.

59. Williams, *Sanctity of Life*, p.287.

60. A. Worcester, *The Care of the Aged, the Dying and the Dead*, Thomas, Springfield, 2nd ed., 1940, p.42.

V *Psychological Aspects*

1. Glanville Williams in Downing, *Euthanasia*, pp.142f.

2. J. Aitken-Swan, *The Practitioner* 183, 1959, p.64.

3. E. Wilkes, *The Lancet*, 1965.1, p.799.

4. C. Saunders in *Matters of Life and Death*, pp.15–26.

5. E. Lindemann, *American Journal of Psychiatry* 101, 1944, p.141.

6. S. R. Lehrmann, *Psychiatric Quarterly* 30, 1956, p.564.

7. Hinton, *Dying*, p.175.

8. C. M. Parkes, *British Journal of Medical Psychology* 38, 1965, p.1.

9. G. Gorer, *Death, Grief and Mourning*, Cresset Press 1965, p.18.

10. M. R. Barrington in Downing, *Euthanasia*, p.167.

11. Williams, *Sanctity of Life*, p.306.

12. G. A. Gresham in Downing, *Euthanasia*, p.149.

13. Ann Cartwright and F. M. Martin, *BMJ* 1959.1, p.779; 1959.2, p.1022.

14. Elizabeth Kübler-Ross, *On Death and Dying*, Tavistock Publications 1970, p.32.

15. Clark-Kennedy, *Man, Medicine and Morality*, p.202.

16. R. Platt, *The Lancet*, 1963.1, p.1.

17. M. Hodson, *Doctors and Patient*, Hodder and Stoughton 1967, pp. 143–58.

18. E. Kübler-Ross, op. cit., p.36.

19. C. Saunders in *Matters of Life and Death*, pp.15–26.

20. E. Kübler-Ross, op. cit., pp.25, 32.

21. W. A. Cramond, *BMJ* 1970.3, p.389.

22. *Postal Symposium* 2, *Management of Terminal Illness*, Smith and Nephew Pharmaceuticals, 1970.

23. H. L. G. Hughes, *Peace at the Last*, Report to the Calouste Gulbenkian Foundation, 1960, p.42.

24. K. Walker, *Patients and Doctors*, Pelican 1957, p.119.

25. Naomi Mitchison, *BMJ* 1965.1, p.186.

26. Gorer, op. cit., p.18.

27. L. J. Raglan, *Journal of the American Medical Association* 147, 1951, p.54.

28. W. D. Kelly and S. R. Friesen, *Surgery* 27, 1950, p.822.

29. B. Gerle and others, *Cancer* 13, 1960, p.1206.

30. *Medical Tribune*, 8 May 1961.

31. J. Norton, *International Psychoanalytic Journal* 18, 1963, p.541.

32. E. Kübler-Ross, op. cit., pp.27, 31f.

33. Cramond, *BMJ* 1970.3, pp.391f.

34. E. Kübler-Ross, op. cit., p.36.

35. Ibid., pp.27, 31f.

36. Ibid., p.28.

37. Ibid., p.29.

38. Ibid., p.37.

39. Ibid., pp.37f.

40. Ibid., p.42.

41. Ibid., p.77.

42. Ibid., p.125.

43. Ibid., p.123.

44. H. C. Shands, *Annals of the New York Academy of Sciences* 125, 1966, p.889.

45. S. E. Waxenberg, ibid., p.1000.

46. S. L. Feder, ibid., p.1020.

47. R. Moses and others, ibid., p.984.

48. L. Le Shan, ibid., p.782.
49. R. Grinker, ibid., p.874.
50. Job 2.9.

VI   *The Principle of Voluntary Euthanasia*

1. Glanville Williams, *Sanctity of Life*, ch. 8, 'Euthanasia', pp.277–312.
2. Antony Flew, 'The Principle of Euthanasia' in Downing, *Euthanasia*, pp.30–48.
3. Joseph Fletcher, *Morals and Medicine*, ch. 6, 'Euthanasia: our Right to Die', pp.172–210; 'The Patient's Right to Die' in Downing, *Euthanasia*, pp.61–70.
4. Fletcher in Downing, *Euthanasia*, pp.66f.
5. Ibid., pp.61f.
6. Fletcher, *Morals and Medicine*, p.205.
7. Williams, *Sanctity of Life*, p.308; cf. also p.303 n.
8. Ibid., p.304.
9. Ibid., p.308.
10. S. L. Henderson, *Medical News-Tribune*, 11 February 1971.
11. Williams, *Sanctity of Life*, p.304.
12. *A Plea for Legislation to Permit Voluntary Euthanasia*, 1970; *Doctors and Euthanasia*, a rejoinder to the BMA's report, printed here as Appendix B.
13. P. Ramsay, *The Patient as Person*, Yale University Press, New Haven, 1970.

VII   *Recent Developments*

1. *BMJ* 1971.1, pp.187f.
2. G. Pickering, ibid., p.193.
3. R. Gillon, 'Suicide and Voluntary Euthanasia: Historical Perspective', in Downing, *Euthanasia*, pp.173–92.
4. *Medical Tribune*, 11 December 1970.
5. *World Medicine*, April 1971, pp.54–9.
6. Ibid., May 1971, p.15.
7. Appendix B, see p.168.
8. *A Plea for Legislation*, pp.9f.